DATE			

B 24771909
i215258113

15

Bilingual Press/Editorial Bilingüe

General Editor
Gary D. Keller

Managing Editor
Karen S. Van Hooft

Senior Editor
Mary M. Keller

Address
Bilingual Press
Box M, Campus Post Office
SUNY-Binghamton
Binghamton, New York 13901
(607) 724-9495

Nosotras
Latina Literature Today

edited by
María del Carmen Boza
Beverly Silva
Carmen Valle

Bilingual Review/Press
BINGHAMTON, NEW YORK

ISBN: 0-916950-63-8
Library of Congress Catalog Card Number: 85-73396

PRINTED IN THE UNITED STATES OF AMERICA

Cover design by Christopher J. Bidlack
Cover illustration by G. Douglas Wood

Acknowledgments

The editors wish to express our gratitude to both the Coordinating Council
of Literary Magazines (CCLM), which awarded this project with a facilitating
grant, and the National Endowment for the Arts (NEA), the parent funding agent.

We would also like to express our thanks to the many editors of journals,
members of writers organizations and other groups, and individuals who
helped us get out the word to Latina writers about this collection.

"The Scholarship Jacket," by Marta Salinas, first appeared in *Cuentos Chicanos:
A Short Story Anthology*, Rudolfo A. Anaya and Antonio Márquez, eds.
(Albuquerque: University of New Mexico Press, 1984).

"The Moths," by Helena María Viramontes, first appeared in *201: Homenaje
a la Ciudad de Los Angeles* (XhismeArte, 1982) and in the author's *The Moths
and Other Stories* (Houston, TX: Arte Público Press, 1985).

Table of Contents

V. Oppression

VI. Galanes

The Authors

Preface

Nosotras: Latina Literature Today is the third anthology of United States Hispanic creative literature to be published by the Bilingual Review/Press. The collections, initiated in 1980 with the publication of *Hispanics in the United States: An Anthology of Creative Literature*, edited by Gary D. Keller and Francisco Jiménez, have had a tangible effect on the world of letters in a number of ways. The books have been in high demand as texts for both college and high school courses. A number of the selections first anthologized in these volumes have been reprinted in important national school editions at both the secondary and college levels. A handful of selections are currently under review for television or film adaptation. The editorial philosophy of the anthologies has received wide praise. For example, reviewers for *Library Journal* observed that whereas most anthologies focus on specific segments of the Hispanic community, the Bilingual Review/ Press format has been able to provide readers with sufficient depth and range to learn about the various Hispanic cultures one finds in the United States.

Nosotras: Latina Literature Today continues the proven editorial philosophy of the Bilingual Review/Press anthology at the same time that the collection focuses on the creative literature of United States Hispanic women. Contributions are present from all the major U.S. Hispanic groups and a wide range of socioeconomic levels and walks of life. The literature anthologized in *Nosotras* provides a good index of the richness of themes, literary personae, and stylistic polyphonies being cultivated by Latina writers in the United States today. The editors of *Nosotras*, María del Carmen Boza, Beverly Silva, and Carmen Valle, bring to the volume not only the expertise of previous publication and high recognition as authors in their own right but also, collectively, the personal foreknowledge of the Chicana, the Cuban-American, and the Puerto Rican experience. Each of the editors has foregone publication of her own material in this anthology in order to ensure her editorial objectivity. The editors had final authority in determining the material that would be included in the anthology, constrained only by the limitations on the number of pages available and the formal requirements of the anthology format.

At the time that material was solicited—and several thousand printed announcements requesting contributions were mailed to individuals and organizations throughout the United States or printed in journals and newsletters—it was stressed that while the literature under consideration had to be written by women and needed to be thematically limited to material dealing with Hispanic life in the United States (including Puerto Rico), in other ways the competition was entirely open. Both established authors as well as first-timers were welcome. There were no constraints on style, language, diction, genre, or ideology. In selecting the works for inclusion, the one criterion to be followed was that of literary merit, an admittedly subjective standard but one that I believe has been admirably met by our three editors in their review and evaluation of the manuscripts that they received.

The collection has been ordered into six categories, representing the thematic patterning of the selections that were accepted for publication. *I. Mind's Eye* emphasizes the literary prerogatives of an incited imagination. *II. Kin* primarily explores the Latina's familial relationships. *III. Bad Vibes* expresses deep, painful personal experiences.

IV. Sage brings us an appreciation of insights, disconcerting ironies, and wisdom, expressed in traditional and nontraditional esthetic forms. *V. Oppression* is about women's rights and human rights and social justice and generic justice. *VI. Galanes* evokes the amorodio, agridulce verities of courtship and amoríos.

   We think that *Nosotras: Latina Literature Today* represents a wide and satisfying swath of both Latina life and creative life in the United States today. We invite you to sample and enjoy the repertoire.

GARY D. KELLER
STATE UNIVERSITY OF NEW YORK
AT BINGHAMTON

I. MIND'S EYE

All the Green Peppers of My Life

Rosa María Arenas

I used to hate green peppers like I hated fried eggs with the yolks running. And I always used to screw up my nose when David ate them raw. But now I have to say how much I really love them, each one.

Last week, the green pepper René brought over in a paper sack had a thick curving stem and on its face a nose, jowls, Richard Nixon. A couple of days ago, we had a green pepper that was a giant's tooth, shaped like a molar in a leaf-green mouth. Just yesterday at Casa Cantú, the Mexican grocery in Holland, Michigan, my mother held up a wrinkled, dark sweet pepper and said it was an old man's "thing," the end pointed and curled like a pig's tail. Today in the kitchen sit two green peppers. One, knobby and hopeless like a twelve-year old's knees; the other, dark, magnificent—a green angel. And when I slice it for an omelette, a pale embryo, the color of a sweet pea, pops out on the plate.

Inside it seems a female place with caverns, three chambers sheltering a cluster of tiny white pepper seeds. Seeds like eggs, like stars or silver dollars on the beach, all mystery. The twisted green pepper in the photograph by Weston on the postcard Sam sends me from San Francisco. And Sam writes how this green pepper reminds him of "the curve along the small of your back." Oh why didn't I think of that?

Genitals and vegetables have been linked since gardening was invented, the green pepper being all sexual organs and more. Green peppers suggesting moonlit dunes, hints of hothouse mingling. Those stems, that smooth dark skin, that small weight almost hollow in the hand, that aroma when sizzling, the way each green pepper yields under the knife, the sweet water it gives under your tongue.

Mi estómago

Marjorie Agosín

Desnuda como en un silencio,
me acerco a mi estómago
ha ido cambiando como un verano
que se aleja del mar,
o como un vestido que se ensancha con las horas.
Mi estómago,
es más que redondo,
porque cuando me siento,
se desparrama como una
llamarada,
entonces,
lo palpo para recordar
todo lo que hay dentro de él:
la sal y la alegría,
los huevos fritos del invierno
la leche que me asfixiaba en la juventud,
la Coca-Cola que marcó mi dentadura
la nostalgia del vaso de vino,
o las papas fritas con aceite de oliva.

Y en el recuerdo,
siento como crece,
y baja cada vez más ceremonioso a la tierra,
hasta le hace cariño a mis pies, a mis dedos
que nunca pudieron ser de princesa.

Yo me alegro
de que mi estómago sea tan ancho como el
sombrero de mis abuelas
en verano.

Este domingo siete,
a los setenta y siete años de edad,
mi estómago,
aún no me lo han quitado
y orgulloso se pasea por el litoral.
Unos dicen que ya estoy vieja y fea,
que mis senos se confunden con mi tripa
pero mi estómago, aquí al ladito mío, acompañándome
y no es grasa lo que desprende
sino trocitos de carne horneándose al sol.

Anticipo

Eliana Rivero

Es cierto:
he muerto tantas veces que debería ser fácil
este nudo de la voz con que respondo
a mi noticia fúnebre

"se ha ido sin sentirlo,
entre papeles, lejanías, estrellitas de polvo
y una ausencia de luz que le robó la vida
lentamente, con furia"

descanso en paz
cuando yo misma leo las palabras
que otros escribirán por mí
después
      en otra parte

They Say

Judith Ortiz Cofer

They say
when I arrived
traveling light,
the women who waited
plugged
the cracks in the walls
with rags
dipped in alcohol
to keep drafts and demons out.
Candles were it
to the Virgin.
They say
Mother's breath
kept blowing them out
right and left.
When I slipped
into their hands
the room was in shadows.
They say
I nearly turned away
undoing
the hasty knot of my umbilicus.
The midwife sewed
and the women prayed
as they fitted
me for life
in a tight corset of gauze.
They say
my urge to bleed
told them I was like a balloon
with a leak,
a soul trying to fly away
through the cracks
in the wall.
But their prayers
held me back,
the bandages held me in,
and all that night
they dipped
their bloody rags.

They say
Mother slept through it all
blowing out
candles
with her breath.

Lluvia

Magaly Quiñones

A lo mejor es otra la que espera
sin piernas tras la lluvia.
A lo mejor es otro el lindero de fuego
que hace frío el calor de mi garganta.
A lo mejor
al cabo de mil años
esa mujer que en sombras ha caído
no seré yo.
Y ese hombre glacial
que se mueve al compás del olvido
traerá otra floración, otra música,
que no llene mis ojos de lágrimas. . . .

A juzgar por el grueso de la lluvia
debo ser yo
quien ha empapado el muro. . . .

II. KIN

A la muerte de un hermano

María Herrera-Sobek

Y
cataplum
te moriste
te sepultamos
te lloramos
clavamos
un clavo
en tu corazón
y dos
en cada uno
de nosotros.
Cerramos
la puerta
la ventana
la caja
tu vida
encerrada
en un cajón gris.
Te
miramos
nos asustamos
te dijimos
adiós
nos fuimos
nos dormimos
te soñamos.
No te habías muerto.
Seguías
con vida
entre la telaraña gris
de la memoria
y nunca más
envejecerás.

Mothering Me

Pat Mora

Right foot, left foot,
right foot, left foot,
I'd say when I held my children's soft
warm hands, teaching them to walk.
At forty I say the words to myself,
right foot, left foot,
right foot, left foot,
I force my feet to move
through sad days of divorce
and lonely love affairs.
I long to stop and simply lie down,
but I push myself forward,
holding my hand, whispering
right foot, left foot

Getting the Boat Ready

Ina Cumpiano

My father says, ¿Qué será de mí de aquí a cien años?
as if he expected an answer. Talking mostly to himself
he sits on the ground near the beach house
sanding his boat. Chickens keep him company,
drawn by the smell of old fish and glue;
a neighbor's cow lows the white egrets off her withers.
I watch his bent back, the way his body follows
the planing thrust of his arms. Not stopping,
he talks about Juan Blos
who lives in a shack by the water
and at eighty still swims out naked every day,
even in the months with an "r" in them.
Yes, I've seen him sitting in a metal folding chair
set in his moored boat, examining the red sea at evening,
as another would a map. My father is startled,
as if he'd forgotten my presence, and works harder;
the surface of the wood is smoothing to glass,
to clear water. Juan's been gone a month now,
really gone, not like the time
he turned up in a bar in Ponce, dead
drunk for weeks. This time the lobsters
in his abandoned traps have eaten each other
and only a claw is left, a carapace,
legs clean as reeds, as sea coral: a sure sign.
Fishermen can tell
changes in the weather while the sky's still clear
by the way the waves ruffle nor'east near the horizon;
how many queen mackerel the net will drag in
by how many pelicans gather and wait in the almendro;
what the year's fishing will be
by its first twelve days (Epiphany is June).
It's not long, my father says,
before Juan Blos' boat is found drifting,
probably by Anselmito, the hunchbacked crab man,
and probably empty.
Back at the Club Náutico, he'll tell how the dinghy,
a pine box on the water, held the remains
of lunch, the bait can rust-dyed the sardines,
the oars rested in place. No weather for miles.

A rough place starboard disappears.
Soon the boat will be ready for varnish.
My father's hands,
God, I notice for the first time,
are corded, and thick through the wrists:
the hands of a man who has spent his life
pulling in nets, rowing, rowing,
and is tiring.
Still, his weather eye is sharp
and I know each night he scans the sky for the disturbance,
for the new light in the school of familiar stars
which will signal good voyage.

The Moths

Helena María Viramontes

I was fourteen years old when Abuelita requested my help. And it seemed only fair. Abuelita had pulled me through the rages of scarlet fever by placing, removing, and replacing potato slices on the temples of my forehead; she had seen me through several whippings, an arm broken by a dare jump off Tío Enrique's toolshed, puberty, and my first lie. Really, I told Amá, it was only fair.

Not that I was her favorite granddaughter or anything special. I wasn't even pretty or nice like my older sisters and I just couldn't do the girl things they could do. My hands were too big to handle the fineries of crocheting or embroidery and I pricked my fingers or knotted my colored threads time and time again while my sisters laughed and called me bull hands with their cute waterlike voices. So I began keeping a piece of jagged brick in my sock to bash my sisters or anyone who called me bull hands. Once, while we all sat in the bedroom, I hit Teresa on the forehead, right above her eyebrow, and she ran to Amá with her mouth open, her hand over her eye, while blood seeped between her fingers. I was used to the whippings by then.

I wasn't respectful either. I even went so far as to doubt the power of Abuelita's slices, the slices she said absorbed my fever. "You're still alive, aren't you?" Abuelita snapped back, her pasty gray eye beaming at me and burning holes in my suspicions. Regretful that I had let secret questions drop out of my mouth, I couldn't look into her eyes. My hands began to fan out, grow like a liar's nose, until they hung by my side like low weights. Abuelita made a balm out of dried moth wings and Vicks and rubbed my hands, shaped them back to size; it was the strangest feeling. Like bones melting. Like sun shining through the darkness of your eyelids. I didn't mind helping Abuelita after that, so Amá would always send me over to her.

In the early afternoon Amá would push her hair back, hand me my sweater and shoes, and tell me to go to Mamá Luna's. This was to avoid another fight and another whipping, I knew. I would deliver one last direct shot on Marisela's arm and jump out of our house, the slam of the screen door burying her cries of anger. I'd gladly go help Abuelita pant her wild lilies or jasmine or heliotrope or cilantro or yerba buena in red Hills Brothers coffee cans, gladly. Abuelita would wait for me on the top step of her porch holding a hammer and nail and empty coffee cans. And although we hardly spoke, hardly looked at each other as we worked over root transplants, I always felt her gray eye upon me. It made me feel, in a strange sort of way, safe and guarded and not alone. Like God was supposed to make you feel.

On Abuelita's porch, I would puncture holes in the bottom of the coffee cans with a nail and a precise hit of the hammer. This completed, my job was to pack them with red clay mud from beneath her rose bushes, packing it softly, then making a perfect hole, four fingers round, to nest a sprouting avocado bone, or the spidery sweet potatoes that Abuelita rooted in mayonnaise jars with toothpicks and daily water, or prickly chayotes that produced vines that twisted and wound all over her porch pillars, crawling to the roof, up and over the roof, and down the other side of her house, making her small brick house look like it was cradled within the vines that grew pear-shaped squashes ready for the pick, ready to be steamed with onions and cheese and butter. The roots would burst out of the rusted coffee cans and search for a place to connect. I would then feed the seedlings with water.

But this was a different kind of help, Amá said, because Abuelita was dying. Looking into her gray eye, then into her brown one, the doctor had said it was just a matter of days. And so it seemed only fair that these hands she had melted and formed found use in rubbing her caving body with alcohol and marijuana, rubbing her arms and legs, turning her face to the window so that she could watch the bird of Paradise blooming or smell the scent of clove in the air. I toweled her face frequently and held her hand for hours. Her gray wiry hair hung over the mattress. Since I could remember she'd kept her long hair in braids. Her mouth was vacant and when she slept her eyelids never closed all the way. Up close, you could see her gray eye beaming out the window, staring hard as if to remember everything. I never kissed her. I left the window open when I went to the market.

Across the street from Jay's Market there was a chapel. I never knew its denominaton, but I went in just the same to search for candles. It's an instinct, I guess. I sat down in one of the pews because there were no candles. After I cleaned my fingernails, I looked up at the high ceiling. I had forgotten the vastness of these places, the coolness of the marble pillars and the frozen statues with blank eyes. I was alone. I knew why I had never returned.

That was one of Apá's biggest complaints. He would pound his hands on the table, rocking the sugar dish or spilling a cup of coffee and scream that if I didn't go to Mass every Sunday to save my goddamn sinning soul, then I had no reason to go out of the house, period. Punto final. He would grab my arm and dig his nails into me to make sure I understood the importance of catechism. Did he make himself clear? Then he strategically directed his anger at Amá for her lousy way of bringing up daughers, being disrespectful and unbelieving, and my older sisters would pull me aside and tell me if I didn't get to Mass right this minute, they were all going to kick the holy shit out of me. Why are you so selfish? Can't you see what it's doing to Amá, you idiot? So I would wash my feet and stuff them in my black Easter shoes that shone with Vaseline, grab a missal and veil, and wave good-bye to Amá.

I would walk slowly down Lorena to First to Evergreen, counting the cracks on the cement. On Evergreen I would turn left and walk to Abuelita's. I liked her porch because it was shielded by the vines of the chayotes so I could get a good look at the people and car traffic on Evergeen without them knowing. I would jump up the porch steps, knock on the screen door as I wiped my feet, and call, "Abuelita? mi Abuelita?" As I opened the door and stuck my head in, I would catch the gagging scent of toasting chile on the placa. When I entered the sala, she would greet me from the kitchen wringing her hands in her apron. I'd sit at the corner of the table to keep from being in her way. The chiles made my eyes water. Am I crying? No, Mamá Luna, I'm sure not crying. I didn't like going to Mass, but my eyes watered anyway, the tears dropping on the tablecloth like candle wax. Abuelita lifted the burnt chiles from the fire and sprinkled water on them until the skins began to separate. Placing them in front of me, she turned to check the menudo. I peeled the skins off, put the flimsy, limp-looking green and yellow chiles in the molcajete, and began to crush and crush and twist and crush the heart out of the tomato, the clove of garlic, the stupid chiles that made me cry, crushed them until they turned into liquid under my bull hand. With a wooden spoon, I scraped hard to destroy the guilt, and my tears were gone. I put the bowl of chile next to a vase filled with freshly cut roses. Abuelita touched my hand and pointed to the bowl of menudo that steamed in front of me. I spooned some chile into the menudo and rolled a corn tortilla thin with the palms of my hands. As I ate, a fine Sunday breeze entered the kitchen and a rose petal calmly feathered down to the table.

I left the chapel without blessing myself and walked to Jay's. Most of the time Jay didn't have much of anything. The tomatoes were always soft and the cans of Campbell soup had rusted spots on them. There was dust on the tops of cereal boxes. I picked up what I needed: rubbing alcohol, five cans of chicken broth, a big bottle of Pine Sol. At first Jay got mad because I thought I had forgotten the money. But it was there all the time, in my back pocket.

When I returned from the market, I heard Amá crying in Abuelita's kitchen. She looked up at me with puffy eyes. I placed the bags of groceries on the table and began putting the cans of soup away. Amá sobbed quietly. I never kissed her. After a while, I patted her on the back for comfort.

"¿Y mi amá?" she asked in a whisper, then choked again and cried into her apron.

"Abuelita fell off the bed twice yesterday," I said, knowing that I shouldn't have said it and wondering why I wanted to say it because it only made Amá cry harder. I guess I became angry and just so tired of the quarrels and beatings and unanswered prayers and my hands just hanging there helplessly by my side. Amá looked at me again, confused, angry, and her eyes were filled with sorrow. I went outside and sat on the porch swing and watched the people pass. I sat there until she left. I dozed off repeating the words to myself like rosary prayers; when do you stop giving when do you start giving when do you . . . and when my hands fell from my lap, I awoke to catch them. The sun was setting, an orange glow, and I knew Abuelita was hungry.

There comes a time when the sun is defiant. Just about the time when moods change, inevitable seasons of a day, transitions from one color to another, that hour or minute or second when the sun is finally defeated, finally sinks into the realization that it cannot, with all its power to heal or burn, exist forever, there comes an illumination where the sun and earth meet, a final defiant burst of burning red orange fury reminding us that although endings are inevitable, they are necessary for rebirths, and when that time came, just when I switched on the light in the kitchen to open Abuelita's can of soup, it was probably then that she died.

The room smelled of Pine Sol and vomit and Abuelita had defecated the remains of her cancerous stomach. She had turned to the window and tried to speak, but her mouth remained open and speechless. I heard you, Abuelita, I said, stroking her cheek, I heard you. I opened the windows of the house and let the soup simmer and overboil on the stove. I turned the stove off and poured the soup down the sink. From the cabinet I got a tin basin, filled it with lukewarm water, and carried it carefully to the room. I went to the linen closet and took out some modest bleached white towels. With the sacredness of handling a priest's vestments, I unfolded the towels one by one on my shoulders. I removed the sheets and blankets from her bed and peeled off her thick flannel nightgown. I toweled her puzzled face, stretching out the wrinkles, removing the coils of her neck, toweled her shoulders and breasts. Then I changed the water. I returned to towel the creases of her stretch-marked stomach, her sporadic vaginal hairs, and her sagging thighs. I removed the lint from between her toes and noticed a mapped birthmark on the fold of her buttock. The scars on her back which were as thin as the life lines on the palms of her hands made me realize how little I really knew of Abuelita. I covered her with a thin blanket and went into the bathroom. I washed my hands and turned on the tub faucets and watched the water pour into the tub with vitality and steam. When it was full, I turned off the water and undressed. Then, I went to get Abuelita.

She was not as heavy as I thought and when I carried her in my arms her body fell into a V; yet, my legs were tired, shaky, and I felt as if the distance between the bedroom and bathroom were miles and years away. Amá, where are you?

I stepped into the bathtub one leg first, then the other. I bent my knees to descend into the water slowly so I wouldn't scald her skin. There, there, Abuelita, I said, cradling her, smoothing her as we descended, I heard you. Her hair fell back and spread across the water like eagle's wings. The water in the tub overflowed and poured onto the tile of the floor. Then the moths came. Small, gray ones that came from her soul and out through her mouth fluttering to light, circling the single dull light bulb of the bathroom. Dying is lonely and I wanted to go to where the moths were, stay with her and plant chayotes whose vines would crawl up her fingers and into the clouds; I wanted to rest my head on her chest with her stroking my hair, telling me about the moths that lay within the soul and slowly eat the spirit up; I wanted to return to the waters of the womb with her so that we would never be alone again. I wanted.

I wanted my Amá. I removed a few strands of hair from Abuelita's face and held her small light head within the hollow of my neck. The bathroom was filled with moths, and for the first time in a long time I cried, rocking us, crying for her, for me, for Amá, the sobs puking the hate from the depths of anguish, the misery of feeling half born, sobbing until finally the sobs rippled into circles and circles of sadness and relief. There, there, I said to Abuelita, rocking us gently, there, there.

El beso de la patria

Sonia Rivera-Valdés

Nos mudamos para Santa Fe cuando yo tenía ocho años. Aunque estábamos muy cerca de La Habana, era otro mundo. El cambio representó un poco de calma porque mi papá y mi mamá no peleaban tanto allí. Era un pueblecito de fuertes contrastes, verde y arenoso, con el mar de la costa norte de la Habana de un lado y las montañas de Tahoro del otro. De los manantiales que hay en esas montañas venía el agua que tomábamos, a tres centavos la lata; después subió a cinco. La lata de agua era inmensa; no sé cuántos litros tenía, pero llenaba una tinaja grande.

Como playa, Santa Fe no valía mucho, demasiadas rocas y poca arena, pero el agua era tan cristalina que yo nadaba despacito por la superficie y veía los peces negros, amarillos, plateados, de todos los colores, paseando por debajo de mí. Uno de mis entretenimientos favoritos era sacar erizos de las rocas del fondo del mar con un palo largo, que generalmente venía de una escoba vieja, al que le ponía un clavo grande en la punta para enganchar los erizos. Me metía en el agua y con la mano derecha sujetaba el palo mientras con la izquierda me apoyaba en un cubilete de madera que tenía el fondo de cristal, para ver adentro del mar, y servía de flotador. Pasaba largas horas en la playa con Rita, la hija de Goyo el pescador, a quien conocí recién mudada al pueblo y nos hicimos grandes amigas. Cuando no estábamos jugando o hablando, me sentaba sobre las rocas a la orilla de la playa, sola, a soñar con el día en que se me rizara el pelo, o en cuando me sacara la lotería para pagar las deudas que mi papá había contraído jugando al póker. El sueño del pelo era el mejor; un día iba a aparecer un hada que me daría una loción mágica, un champú milagroso que me rizaría el pelo para siempre. No me gustaba mi pelo, lacio y fino; quería uno de aquellos con muchos bucles que veía en el cine de Hollywood; mi preferido era el de Viveca Lindfors en una película en que hacía de gitana.

En invierno el mar rompía con tanta fuerza contra las rocas, que una señora que estaba de visita un fin de semana preguntó si había alguna fábrica cerca, cuyas maquinarias producía la gente que venía de vacaciones, como una gran bandada de pájaros que se iba al llegar septiembre. Para julio o agosto armaban el parque de diversiones; venían unos hombres, desyerbaban un terreno grande en alguno de los lugares más céntricos, generalmente un solar vacío de los que bordeaban la carretera de Santa Fe a Punta Brava, e instalaban los caballitos, la estrella, las sillas voladoras, el kiosco del algodón de azúcar, los puestos de frituras y refrescos, los de vender cerveza y los de juegos de azar, en los que se podía ganar un muñeco de peluche, una taza con su plato, o una polvera de cristal que tenía en la tapa una gallina echada . . . ésas eran lindas. Instalaban centenares de bombillos; el día de la inauguración, para los que vivíamos permanentemente en la playa, acostumbrados a largos meses de calles silenciosas y semi apagadas, era el deslumbramiento; el movimiento y la iluminación nos maravillaban; recibíamos el parque con tanto entusiasmo que se llenaba todas las noches durante el tiempo que permanecía. Después, cuando comenzaba a oscurecer más temprano y a amanecer más tarde, y el mar empezaba a oírse desde la casa por las noches, un día veíamos con melancolía cómo los hombres que desyerbaron el terreno desarmaban los aparatos y desmontaban el parque. Al poco tiempo sobre la tierra apisonada por los pies de la gente volvía a crecer la yerba.

Rita y yo íbamos juntas a la escuela pública. Su mamá, Julia, era la conserje y como ella era quien preparaba y repartía la merienda, siempre me daba mucha. Daban leche condensada con gofio en la sesión de la tarde a la que asistíamos porque los varones iban por la mañana. Aunque se suponía que la merienda fuera sólo para las niñas más necesitadas y yo no lo era, porque las había que no comían en su casa, mi amistad con Rita garantizaba mi parte, lo que me ponía muy contenta.

Yo estaba en cuarto grado. Fue el primero que hice completo en una misma escuela, ya que anteriormente debido a las mudadas constantes y a que a mi mamá no le gustaba levantarse temprano para mandarme a las clases, cambiaba tres o cuatro veces de escuela durante un curso escolar, y a veces faltaba meses completos. Esa fue, también, la primera vez que tomé exámenes para pasar de grado. Por las mañanas, sentada en el piso de mosaicos rojos y blancos del portal de la casita de madera en que vivíamos, que se mantenían fríos aunque hubiera un sol que rajaba las piedras, memorizaba cuanto había escrito en los cuadernos el día anterior. Era la experiencia más grata que había tenido en mi vida. Leyendo sobre las guerras de independencia de Cuba en el siglo XIX, o aprendiendo cuáles eran los ríos más caudalosos de Europa, o qué animales tenían sangre caliente y cuáles la tenían fría, o cuántos huesos tenía el cuerpo humano, olvidaba un rato los llantos de mi mamá encerrada en el baño, por razones que yo sólo medio entendía, y la falta de dinero de la que mi papá hablaba constantemente. Mientras leía, sentía el fresco del piso en mis muslos y piernas, oía cantar los pájaros y miraba, cada vez que interrumpía la lectura, las vicarias blancas y rojas y las madamas sembradas en el jardincito frente al portal, del cual mi papá y todos nosotros habíamos sacado las piedras y latas vacías que tenía cuando nos mudamos allí y habíamos sembrado flores. Pensaba en lo maravillosas que eran las flores de la vicaria blanca, capaces de curar enfermedades de los ojos, y en lo curiosas que eran las vainitas en que se formaban las semillas de la madama.

Nunca tuve espíritu de competencia porque no tenía por qué desarrollarlo. Mi mamá no me exigía nada en ese sentido, y con tantos cambios ni siquiera sabía que existían premios si se tenían buenas notas. Aquel año gané el Beso de la Patria, premio que daban al mejor alumno de cada grado. Me sorprendí muchísimo cuando lo recibí porque no lo esperaba, pero me dio una gran alegría. Debido a este premio fui elegida para llevar el estandarte de la escuela en el natalicio de Martí del próximo año. Era un reconocimiento a mi excelente trabajo académico. Para conmemorar el veintiocho de enero se organizaban enormes paradas. Los colegios privados hacían un despliegue de lujo con uniformes de gala y bandas de música en que los niños iban vestidos de satín rojo, azul pavo, azul prusia, verde brillante, amarillo canario, y los trajes estaban adornados con galones de colores contrastantes; en la cabeza llevaban sombreros altos con penachos de plumas; competían a ver cuál colegio iba más elegante. Las escuelas públicas, iban aparte; trataban de que los niños se vistieran lo mejor posible y ponían algunas restricciones para poder asistir; había que usar cierta ropa que muchos no tenían; ésos no podían participar en el acto patriótico; un requisito era tener el uniforme de la escuela; la mayoría de los alumnos iba a las clases sin uniforme; los maestros, generalmente, no lo exigían porque sabían que si los niños no lo compraban era porque no tenían dinero para hacerlo. Cuando me nombraron para llevar el estandarte, lo que era un gran honor, me advirtieron que era necesario ir uniformada y llevar zapatos de piel o charol negro. Yo tenía un uniforme que alguien me había regalado usado; mi mamá lo había teñido para que recuperara el color original y lucía muy bien, pero mis únicos zapatos eran unos tenis. Cuando me dijeron lo de los zapatos no me atreví a decir que no los tendría porque me daba mucha pena y dije que sí, que iba a tenerlos. No pensé en otra cosa por un mes y pico, hasta que llegó el día; no se me olvidaba ni cuando estudiaba por la mañana en el portal; no conseguía alegrarme ni escuchando el canto de los pájaros, ni aunque los mosaicos estuvieran fríos como siempre, ni aunque las semillas de las madamas hubieran hecho su trabajo de fecundidad con tal constancia que había muchas maticas nuevas; lloraba todos los días donde no me vieran y no dije nada en mi casa porque sabía que no iba a haber zapatos negros. Finalmente llegó el día, y después de pensarlo mucho decidí ir; me arreglé lo mejor que pude, muy bañadita y peinada, con lazos grandes en las trenzas, medias blancas, y lavé los tenis. Al presentarme, en medio de la confusión de la organización de la parada, no notaron nada, pero al prepararnos para empezar la marcha yo iba sola delante de los otros estudiantes. Al ver mis pies, una de las maestras, una señora vieja que decían que era poeta, me llamó aparte y me dijo: "Tú sabes que sin zapatos negros no puedes llevar el estandarte. Nosotros entendemos que no los tienes y por eso no los has traído, pero la parada tiene que quedar bonita. Mira, lo que vamos a hacer es que entre todos los maestros vamos a reunir dinero para comprarte unos zapatos para la próxima vez. Ahora, Noemí llevará el estandarte." Noemí, que era brutísima y sacaba malísimas notas, tenía zapatos de charol con unos lacitos de faya. Lloré disimuladamente toda la parada. Lo que más me dolía era lo que dijo la maestra de que iban a regalarme unos zapatos. Me pareció todo terriblemente injusto, que yo estaba pagando culpas que no había cometido. Sufría calladamente cada vez que entraba a la escuela en los días posteriores a la parada, pensando en el momento en que me fueran a dar los benditos zapatos. Pero mis angustias estaban de más, porque jamás reunieron ningún dinero ni me compraron ningunos zapatos.

Mi tía Zoila

Sonia Rivera-Valdés

Los domingos venían a visitarnos mi tía Zoila, mi tío Cunín y mi prima Lucina. Lucina era hija única, cuatro años mayor que yo y había nacido por cesárea. La madre por poco muere del parto porque eso fue en Güines, en los tiempos en que una cesárea era cosa de vida o muerte. El médico que la atendió consideró un milagro que se hubieran salvado ella y la niña y, demostrando muy poco respeto por los santos católicos, la bautizó con el nombre de Lucina, en honor a la diosa del parto romana.

Aparte de las visitas de los domingos, mi tía Zoila pasaba temporadas en mi casa con frecuencia. Tío Cunín se quedaba en La Habana, donde vivían, porque tenía que trabajar en la tabaquería y cuidar a la niña, que ya estaba grandecita. Tía Zoila venía porque su salud, bastante precaria, mejoraba en la playa, según ella. Me gustaba mucho que viniera porque cuando estaba mis padres peleaban menos, aunque a veces no les importaban los testigos y se insultaban en la misma forma que lo hacían cuando estábamos solos. Entonces tía Zoila recogía sus cosas, siempre lo último la sombrilla que llevaba aunque no lloviera, y no abría aunque el sol quemara, y sin despedirse de ellos, de mí sí lo hacía, se iba para su casa, aun cuando su salud empeorara. Yo no quería que se fuera, quería desesperadamente que se quedara. Su presencia me acompañaba y protegía. Delante de ella mi papá no iba a atreverse a matar a mi mamá. Ese era el miedo último, el que estaba detrás de todos los otros miedos. Pero cuando decía: "Sonia, me voy, hasta pronto," y me besaba, yo sólo respondía: "Hasta luego, tía," y la besaba. Sabía que era inútil pedirle que se quedara. Todos siempre hacían lo que querían, para eso eran personas mayores.

Tía Zoila tenía muchas enfermedades, sabía muchas cosas, hacía muchos cuentos. Me entretenía más ella que Lucina, una niña sin cuentos interesantes ni sufrimientos. ¿Qué podía haber sufrido si su papá nunca amenazó de muerte a su mamá?

De los cuentos de tía Zoila, uno de mis favoritos era el de un baile al que fue en el campo, allá por Báez, donde se crió. Un grupo de campesinos se reunió en un bohío para hacer una fiesta; entonces un guajiro cogió una guitarra y empezó a tocarla y a cantar:

> Ven, ven, canario ven,
> ven, ven, canario ven,

y al son de este estribillo todos bailaron por horas y horas, sin añadir una sílaba a aquella frase ni cambiar la tonada. Tía Zoila dramatizaba el cuento; actuaba cada parte de la historia, imitaba al guajiro tocando la guitarra y bailaba como lo hacían las parejas.

Además de la cesárea, la mamá de Lucina había sido operada de la vesícula, de un fibroma y de no recuerdo cuántas cosas más. Padecía un montón de alergias y cuando tenía más de cuarenta años se le desarrolló un asma bastante molesta. Ibamos al cine a menudo, ella y yo solas. Cuando en Sante Fe el cine costaba diez centavos, íbamos casi todas las noches. No importaba la película que pusieran, ella siempre le encontraba algo cómico hasta a la más trágica. Como yo sabía que no tomaba nada en serio pasaba grandes trabajos para ocultar las lágrimas que derramaba a borbotones en las películas tristes. Llevaba al cine la sombrilla (tal vez sentía que la sombrilla la protegía) y una cartera grande. En la cartera cargaba un botiquín de medicinas.

En medio de la función sacaba las gotas para la nariz y se las ponía. Guardaba el pomito. Al poco rato, sacaba una botella con una medicina antialérgica, para so sé qué alergia, y una cucharita y tomaba una o dos cucharadas. Guardaba la botella. Al rato, y aquí venía lo peor, pensaba yo, sacaba un aparato que tenía una bombita de goma que ella apretaba mientras tenía el aparato adentro de la boca. Era para el asma. Al apretar la bomba de goma aire que salía hacía ruido y la gente nos miraba, volteando la cabeza los que estaban en las filas delante de nosotras, y la mandaban a callar. Ella parecía no enterarse de nada. Terminaba y guardaba el aparato en la cartera. Yo trataba de hacerme la desentendida, pero seguía paso por paso el proceso que me divertía y horrorizaba al mismo tiempo porque sabía exactamente cuando iban a empezar a mirarnos y a callarla. Esto lo hacía cada vez que íbamos al cine.

Tía Zoila vivía en la calle Monserrate 409, en La Habana Vieja, frente al Instituto de Segunda Enseñanza de La Habana. Era un edificio viejo, de cuatro pisos, con los techos altos y una enormidad de escalones entre un piso y otro que había que subir caminando. De nueva fue una de esas casas elegantes de La Habana con balcones de hierro hermosamente trabajado; de vieja, la habían dividido para alquilar las habitaciones por separado. Cada piso tenía un balcón al frente que daba a la calle Monserrate, seguido de dos amplios aposentos que habían servido de sala y saleta en la antigüedad y que, para el tiempo en que yo conocí la casa, funcionaban a modo de vestíbulo. Al final del vestíbulo había una puerta grande con vitrales en los bordes y encima, que daba a un pasillo rematado por un balcón interior de linda balaustrada, tan oxidada y cubierta de hollín que era necesario observarla detenidamente para apreciar el fino trabajo. Las habitaciones de los inquilinos ocupaban ambos lados del vestíbulo y bordeaban el pasillo del balcón de adentro. Era la distribución típica de la mayoría de las construcciones coloniales. El balcón del frente era compartido por todos los vecinos que iban allí a coger aire cuando se sentían asfixiados en los mal ventilados cuartos. Solamente a las doce del día entraba el sol al edificio. En la mayoría de las habitaciones la claridad del día era tan tenue que había que encender los bombillos desde por la mañana.

En la planta baja había una fonda de chinos. Desde el pedazo del balcón interior que quedaba frente al cuarto de tía Zoila se veía la parte de atrás de la fonda; para los dueños del restaurante aquella zona de la casa era un patio que les servía de desahogo para la cocina, y allí pelaban las papas, preparaban los vegetales, escamaban el pescado, picaban la carne, escogían el arroz y los frijoles, lavaban los platos y las cazuelas, y fumaban sentados con las piernas abiertas, la lata del tabaco entre las piernas, una pipa larga con la que inhalaban el humo por la nariz y chancletas de palo. Cuando yo me quedaba en casa de tía Zoila, pasaba largos ratos mirándolos; desde el balcón del tercer piso aquellas figuritas lejanas lucían irreales, como las escenas de una película sobre lugares remotos o las imágenes de un sueño.

A veces mi tío Cunín y yo almorzábamos en la fonda. Yo pedía pescado "sobreuso" porque me gustaba el nombre. Me parecía magia que trajeran un pescado con salsa de tomate por encima cuando pronunciaba aquella palabra, "sobreuso." Entendía la relación entre sonidos como, pescado frito o pescado asado y las comidas que respondían a estos términos; muchas otras cosas se asaban y freían: papas, plátanos, carnes, pero nunca entendí qué significaba "sobreuso." Pensaba en algo que se usaba de nuevo, pero el pescado parecía recién cocinado, y que nadie antes que yo lo había usado. Esperaba que un día, al pedirlo, alguien iba a revelarme el misterio. En vez de una comida me traerían una explicación, pero nunca pasó, y todos creyeron firmemente que yo adoraba aquel plato porque lo ordenaba repetidamente. Mi curiosidad insatisfecha me llevó a buscar la palabra en un diccionario; no la encontré, pero en un *Larousse* estaba "sobreasada" y decía que era lo mismo que "sobrasada," y sobrasada era una salchicha. Entonces pensé que a lo mejor "sobreuso" era, correctamente, "sobruso" y que los dueños de la fonda, como eran chinos, se habían equivocado al escribir en español. Busqué "sobruso" y tampoco apareció. Ya en este punto me di por vencida y clasifiqué la palabra entre las misteriosas de comidas. Total, no era la primera vez que no entendía los nombres de algunos platos. Decidí que "sobreuso" era como "ropa vieja," no había explicación posible.

En la mayoría de los cuartos del edificio de tía Zoila vivían parejas. Los únicos niños que habían crecido allí en muchos años eran mi prima Lucina y los hijos de los encargados del edificio, unos españoles que tenían un niño y una niña más blancos que el papel. Los encargados habían unido tres habitaciones contiguas del segundo piso para hacer un apartamento. A la izquierda de tía Zoila había un muchacho joven que sólo frecuentaba el edificio los fines de semana o algunas noches y siempre iba con otro muchacho, pero no con la misma persona. Había un señor alto y gordo que usaba su cuarto, en el segundo piso, para ver a la amante de turno. A la derecha de tía Zoila vivía Teresa, una francesa que había sido prostituta por años, pero que ahora dirigía un prostíbulo porque ya estaba vieja. Su marido, un hombre muy elegante, cubano, que la había "protegido" durante los años azarosos de duro trabajo, era camarero en el cabaret Montmartre. Al cabo de años de estar juntos, le decía: "Teresa, basta ya, ¿por qué no te quedas en la casa y descansas?" "Porque me aburriría, contestaba ella, y esto es lo único que sé hacer." Finalmente la convenció para que se casaran y así ella pudiera cobrar el retiro de él, si moría antes que ella. Teresa vestía siempre de negro, el pelo hacia atrás con un moño en la nuca y se pintaba los ojos muy negros. Hablaba bajito arrastrando las erres: "Tienes que estudiar," me decía en las largas conversaciones que sosteníamos en el balcón que daba a la calle Monserrate. "Tú no sabes cuánto han trabajado estas manos por no saber yo hacer otra cosa." Ella ignoraba que tía Zoila me había dicho cuál era su verdadera profesión, y cada vez que decía esto yo pensaba, mirándola seria y mostrando mucha atención a lo que decía: "No está diciendo la verdad, si nunca ha trabajado con las manos." Para mí, Teresa era un ser misterioso y fascinante a quien respetaba porque siempre me trataba con cariño. Me hubiera gustado que me contara de su verdadero trabajo, pero nunca lo hizo. Ella y el esposo jamás peleaban delante de la gente. Yo me preguntaba cómo serían cuando estaban solos.

En el cuarto piso, en una de las habitaciones del frente, vivía otra francesa con su marido, Susana, prostituta también. Se daban unas borracheras formidables. Cuando se emborrachaban peleaban y gritaban por horas, pero como lo hacían en francés, porque él era también francés, los vecinos nunca entendieron el porqué de las peleas. Un día tía Zoila regresaba del trabajo, como a las cuatro y media o las cinco. Al acercarse al edificio vio un grupo grande de gente arremolinado junto a la puerta de entrada mirando para adentro, unos por sobre las cabezas de los otros. Tía Zoila se asustó porque pensó que habría ocurrido alguna desgracia. Se acercó y se empinó en la punta de los pies para ver qué pasaba. Vio a Susana saliendo por la puerta; había decidido dar un paseo por La Habana, pero iba completamente desnuda. En el momento en que salía a la calle, rodeada del gentío asombrado, llegaba el marido, que se dirigía a su cuarto. Al verla sin ropa, no se inmutó, tranquilamente se quitó el saco, pues siempre andaba con traje, envolvió a Susana en él, amarrándole en la espalda las mangas a modo de tirantes, la volteó suavemente y la empujó despacito hacia la escalera para que subiera de nuevo. Ella obedeció sin protestar porque estaba muy borracha y subió enseñando las nalgas, porque el saco solamente allí tapaba por delante. Tía Zoila, que permanecía callada entre los espectadores, siguió de largo por la acera con todos ellos cuando la francesa entró, comentando con los demás: "¡Qué barbaridad, esa mujer encuerada en el medio de la calle, y con lo flaca y vieja que está!" Anduvo como una cuadra en lo que cada uno seguía su camino; entonces dio media vuelta, y regresó para el edificio, cerciorándose antes de entrar de que no estuviera ninguno de los que habían contemplado el espectáculo. Algún tiempo después Susana y el marido se sacaron el primer premio de la lotería; jugaban todas las semanas con la esperanza de ganar y volver a Francia con aquel dinero; así lo hicieron. Unos meses más tarde las francesas del barrio le contaron a tía Zoila que Susana había cogido un día, en su país, una borrachera más grande que las habituales para celebrar el regreso y en medio de la fiesta se tiró por el balcón del hotel en que se hospedaba.

En el cuarto de enfrente del de tía Zoila vivía una mexicana que había llegado a Cuba años atrás con un amante cubano; él la abandonó, y como no sabía trabajar en nada se dedicó a cuidar hijos de prostitutas. Los niños vivían con ella; cuando las madres podían, los venían a ver los fines de semana, a veces un ratico los domingos. Sólo cuidaba uno a la vez, generalmente niñas pequeñas, de dos o tres años, que corrían y jugaban a las muñecas en el pasillo oscuro del balcón interior al que daban los cuartos. Amanda, que así se llamaba la señora, era cariñosa con las niñas, trataba de alimentarlas bien haciéndoles muchas sopas, y no les pegaba. Cuando por alguna razón, porque la madre se mudaba, le iba mal en el negocio, se enfermaba, o moría, le quitaban el niño que cuidaba, Amanda lo pasaba muy mal en lo que conseguía otro, pero por suerte para ella había tantas prostitutas con hijos que no podían cuidar, que casi nunca estaba sin trabajo. Amanda me contaba que, cuando estaba sola, a veces se desvelaba. El cuarto, que era muy pequeñito, se le hacía una prisión, entonces se iba a caminar, a cualquier hora que fuera. Le gustaba sentarse en la escalinata del Capitolio. Al principio, los policías se acercaban a preguntarle qué hacía allí y la mandaban para otra parte, pero después se hizo amiga de ellos y pasaban largas horas conversando, a veces hasta las cuatro o las cinco de la mañana, en que el sol ya iba a salir y a ella le parecía que el cuarto no era tan chiquito cuando estaba un poquito claro. Regresaba y dormía un rato; después se levantaba, tomaba café, y salía a recorrer los protíbulos cercanos para conseguir otro niño que cuidar. Le pagaban dos pesos diarios. Ella decía que eso mismo pagaban a las empleadas del Ten Cent, y tenían que usar medias y faja para trabajar, así que su sueldo era mejor, porque podía ponerse cualquier ropa.

Mi papá, que era hermano de tía Zoila, insistía en que se mudara de allí, pero ella se negaba. Sólo pagaba cuatro pesos mensuales de alquiler, y le gustaba el sitio; estaba bien localizado y quería a sus vecinas, quienes compartían con ella lo que cocinaban, y no eran chismosas. Le gustaba dormir la mañana cuando no trabajaba y allí podía hacerlo sin que nadie la molestara, pues todos se levantaban tarde. La vida en el edificio comenzaba sobre las tres o las cuatro de la tarde, con la excepción de los niños, y éstos habían aprendido a jugar callados. Todo el mundo se levantaba después del mediodía por diferentes razones; tal vez influía el que los cuartos eran tan oscuros que sus ocupantes perdían la noción del tiempo.

Tía Zoila había sido sietemesina, y por eso pesaba una libra y media cuando nació. Decía que la comadrona la puso sobre una mesa, pensando que moriría en pocos minutos, y no se ocupó de ella; comenzó a atender a mi abuela, momentos después, su papá entró en la habitación para ver qué pasaba y vio que la niña se movía y lloraba bajito. Se lo dijo a la comadrona, quien entonces cogió a la niña, la limpió, la envolvió en algodones y se la dio a mi abuela. Mi abuela, que era gorda de joven y con unos senos muy grandes, cargó a su hija adentro del escote por más de tres meses, para darle calor. La niña no mamaba hasta que tuvo más de tres meses. Abuela, para alimentarla, extraía leche de su pecho, la echaba en un platico y la ponía en la boca de la bebita con un gotero. Cuando tía Zoila tenía doce o trece años una maestra de la escuela a donde iba, en Báez, quiso enviarla a estudiar a Santa Clara, la capital de la provincia. Decía la maestra que la niña era muy inteligente. Mi abuelo no la dejó ir; a ella nunca se le olvidó; ya de mujer, trabajaba en el despalillo de tabaco en una fábrica grande, H. Upman, y le gustaba vestirse bien, a su manera. Usaba muchos vestidos de sol, con los hombros desnudos y zapatos franceses, que decía que eran los únicos que soportaba. Los zapatos eran siempre sin talón porque decía que tenía los pies muy delicados. Compraba la ropa en los colores que más lindos encontraba, sin importarle que no fueran los más discretos y apropiados para una señora habanera de más de cuarenta años de edad. Jamás prestó atención a las críticas. Ella y Lucina no se llevaban muy bien, creo que porque no tenía vocación de madre, pero, para mí era una gran amiga, muy divertida; y como yo estaba acostumbrada a que mi mamá me contara sus penas y sus problemas, sin darse cuenta de que quien escuchaba aquellas amarguras medía dos pies y medio de estatura y tenía siete u ocho años . . . Sin embargo, mi prima Lucina se llevaba muy bien con mi mamá. Iban juntas al dentista, a la modista, a las tiendas, a los mandados. Mi mamá invitaba a Lucina a salir con ella; antes que a mí, y mi tía Zoila me invitaba a mí antes que a Lucina. En medio de todo, mi prima y yo éramos dichosas porque aunque teníamos las madres cruzadas se ocupaban mucho de nosotras, ya que nos necesitaban para que les hiciéramos compañía. Cuando mi tía no hablaba de sus enfermedades o contaba la vida de sus vecinos, hacía chistes. Tal vez le dolía demasiado hablar en serio.

De Santa Fe recuerdo las mañanas, que parecía que las limpiaban antes de que amaneciera para que lucieran bonitas al salir el sol. Recuerdo el puestecito en donde vendían guarapo, los higos de patios ajenos que comíamos Rita y yo al regresar de la escuela, los mangos, las frutabombas, la carretera a Cangrejeras, por la que montaba una bicicleta vieja que compartíamos mi hermano y yo. Era una carretera con inmensos árboles a ambos lados, tan frondosos, que sus copas se unían sobre el camino dando una romántica penumbra al lugar. Yo anhelaba furiosamente que ése fuera el escenario de un desengaño amoroso inolvidable, pero nunca pasó nada. También era hermosa la lluvia de Santa Fe, y los atardeceres en que el sol bajaba al final del mar, rojo y despacito. Desde el viejo puente de madera de la casa de Rita, que daba a donde el sol se ponía, yo cerraba los ojos antes de que se ocultara, tratando de capturar aquella imagen en mi imaginación para el futuro. Pensaba que sería un buen recuerdo para consolarme en los momentos malos y en los días grises.

De La Habana me gustaban las calles estrechas: Lamparilla, Obrapía, Obispo, por cuyas aceras era peligroso caminar cuando pasaban las guaguas. Había que pegarse a la pared, lo que me daba miedo, pero encontraba emocionante. Me gustaban las tiendas de polacos, que más tarde averigüé que eran libaneses en su gran mayoría; vendían telas, botones, hilos, encajes de diferentes estilos; me gustaban los olores de las fondas, sobre todo el olor de la fonda de chinos de los bajos de tía Zoila, y el perfume que salía de una peluquería de la calle Obispo, Dubic, donde vendían agua de Portugal e iban los amantes de las francesas a arreglarse las uñas.

Un día, yendo en guagua por Lamparilla, tía Zoila me hizo muchos cuentos. Me dijo que sabía cuando estaba muy nerviosa porque le daba miedo el espíritu de su mamá que había muerto años antes. También me dijo que no podía comer carne de puerco, por eso comía tanto carnero; se operó de la vesícula, pero continuó sin poder comer carne de puerco. En una ocasión una vecina estaba haciendo carnero, ella vio que era carnero, pues así y todo, cuando la comida estuvo lista, no pudo comerla porque pensó que a lo mejor el carnero se había convertido en puerco en la cazuela e iba a hacerle daño; fue al médico y le contó el episodio; él la mandó a un siquiatra; el siquiatra le recetó que leyera un libro de novecientas páginas titulado *Los estados nerviosos de angustia,* de Wilhelm Steckel; no lo leyó porque le daba miedo mirarse por dentro, según decía, y me lo regaló. Lo leí dos veces completo y entendí muchas cosas sobre mi tía Zoila y sobre mi mamá y sobre mí con aquel libro, aunque no explicaba todo lo que yo quería saber. De cualquier forma, fue una pena que ella nunca lo leyera. Para ese entonces yo ya tenía como trece años.

Please, Yell "Bingo!"

Raquel Puig Zaldívar

Westi had never owned a brand new dress. However, there was a special pride in her eyes when she put the best one she had on top of her bed. One of the ladies she had worked for had given it to her; Westi could never have imagined a more magnificent piece of clothing. She had worn it to the most memorable occasions she had lived in those eight years; the day she got married, the day each of her seven children had been baptized, the day her oldest son had died, and that Wednesday night to go to the bingo game.

Westi had been saving for two months to pay for her place at the game. It would have cost her five dollars! She touched the space between her breasts, inside her bra, the safest place she could find. That's where she was hiding her money. Twenty dollars a month, six children to feed and no husband, no wonder it had taken her two months to save it!

Her husband had left her, for God knows whom, six months before. He had gone to work one day and never returned. His clothes were gone too, that's when she suspected something. Then the bus driver who was married to her mother's cousin told her that he had seen her husband with a suitcase and — it had been hard for him to say it — with another woman! The bastard! Leaving her like that, without even buying the bed she needed for their children.

Seven people can't sleep on a full mattress. That was all she had. Then, like a miracle — she could swear it was a miracle — someone told her about the bingo game. Dozens of people from all over town went every Wednesday. Each card cost five pesos, and if you won, you could get thirty, seventy-five or one hundred fifty pesos! Westi had never seen that much money in her whole life.

At eight o'clock that morning, her two oldest boys were shining shoes downtown; her six-year-old sold peanuts and took his four-year-old brother with him. Westi took her two little girls to work with her every day.

"Mamá, where are we going?" Susan asked the same question every morning.

"To work, darling, Mamá has to work all day. Did you eat your bread yet?"

"Kind of," her shiny black eyes smiled mischievously. "You know how Lenny gives me cookies every time we go. I still have the rest of the bread in my pocket, just in case."

"Did your sister eat it all?"

"Where are we going with that dress, Mamá?" the little girl asked, pointing at the bed.

"To the bingo game." Just saying it seemed like an accomplishment.

"What's a bingo game?"

"That's where a man calls out numbers, and at the end some people win a lot of money. Today, I'm going to win enough to buy us another bed, perhaps two beds, if Mamá gets lucky." The child clapped and helped Westi straighten out the creases in the yellow dress.

"Okay, Susan, let's go."

Westi touched the five dollars she had placed in her bosom. She had to remember to ask Lenny all about the game. She knew her numbers well, there was no reason why she shouldn't know how to play, but she wanted to know the rules. And anyway, she had asked the Virgin to help her. Westi knew she had to win that Wednesday.

With her two long black braids wrapped around her head like a crown, Westi walked to work with her little girls that morning. She had never known anything other than the zinc walls and roofs of the shabby houses on her street. Her husband had married her in Santa Fe when she was fifteen, and they had moved to San Pedro right away.

"Mamá, why is your name Westi and mine Susan and Cheli's, Cheli?" Her daughter's question interrupted her thoughts.

"Oh, Susan, when I was waiting for God to send you to me, I used to work for a nice lady. She gave me money to buy you some clothes and sheets to cover you. By the time you came, we had used up all the baby clothes your brothers wore. This lady's name was Susan, so I named you Susan."

"Can we go and visit Susan now?"

"No, she's not here any more. She finished school and went away."

"Away where? To the capital?"

"No, to a country so far away that you have to take an airplane to get there. That's where Lenny lives too."

"Is he going to go away?"

"Not right now, but when he's through."

"What's an airplane?"

"You ask too many questions, Susan, c'mon, walk quickly and let's try to get to work fast."

The streets of San Pedro were full of street vendors. Trucks full of green bananas, carrots and onions glided by waiting for housewives or maids to stop them to buy something. The newspaper man called out, "Caribe!" in front of each house, hoping to stop and make a sale. Barefoot black boys walked by with cans full of peanuts calling out to sell their products: "¡Manicero, maní! ¡Manicero, maní!" Westi thought of her two sons and wished she could find a way to send them to school and keep them from wasting themselves in the streets like that. She was ignorant and poor, but she knew that was a waste. Now, with no husband, there was little she could do, except pray. Well, perhaps one day . . . right then, there was only one thought on her mind: She had to win some money at the bingo game and buy her children at least one bed. After two months of hard work to save those five dollars . . . She put her hand over her chest to feel the money once more.

Miramar is San Pedro's largest student neighborhood. It would never have been built unless the university had opened a department of medicine ten years before and had made it available to American students. In ten years the word had spread and there were over 2,000 trying to become doctors. Lenny was one of them.

"Don Lenny, open up, it's me, Westi."

The two little girls and the woman waited at the door until they heard steps, and then the sound of the door opening.

"Good morning! You look tired, Lenny!" Westi went straight to the kitchen while Susan and Cheli greeted their American friend.

"I have a reason to be, Westi." Lenny sat in the rocking chair with Cheli on his knees while Susan searched the magazine basket for a picture of a cowboy.

"Studying hard, eh?" Westi's voice could be heard over the sounds of the water and the dishes.

"No, it wasn't that. I was robbed last night. 250 pesos! All I had for the rest of the term! And we still have a month to go!"

"Pray to the Virgin, Lenny, that's what I do when I don't have money, and something good always happens."

"Not even the Virgin will fix this mess. I won't be able to pay the rent, or food . . . or even you, Westi. Don't you think it's serious?"

"Yes, it's serious." Westi sounded worried for a moment, but in seconds her voice became cheerful again. "Anyway, pray to the Virgin, Lenny. She can help."

"I'm Jewish, Westi," he said, smiling, putting the little girl on the floor and walking to the kitchen. "The Virgin won't work for us."

"You're saying that because you don't really know the Virgin. She works for everyone! Listen, do you remember what I told you once?"

"What?"

"The bingo game!"

"What bingo game?"

"The one they play in town every Wednesday."

"What about it?"

"Well, do you have five pesos?"

"Yes,"

"Well, try your luck. You might win some money that way."

"And if I lose?" Lenny replied doubtfully.

"Pray to the Virgin; I told you she can help."

Lenny raised one of his eyebrows questioningly.

"Well," Westi was tring her best to find a good answer. "Don't pray to the Virgin, then, I'll pray to her for you. Go to the bingo game. I'm going!" she added proudly.

"You? It's five pesos!"

"I know," she answered vainly, patting the bundle inside her blouse. "I've been saving for the past two months, and now I have it." Then she shrugged her shoulders and looked apologetic. "I need a bed for my kids, you know, and I can think of no other decent way of buying one." She smiled and closed the door.

"Westi," he called again.

The young man sat back on his desk chair holding a pencil close to his lips. The maid opened the door and peeked in once more.

"Yes?"

"I'll go to the bingo game tonight. Pray to your Virgin."

"That's fine," she said and quickly closed the door.

"Westi," Lenny said once more.

"Yes?" she answered, coming back.

"Have you ever thought of going to school?"

"Oh no, Don Lenny," she laughed. "I stopped going in the third grade. I began to work with my mother then. After that, I got married. Now I have six children. We are too poor to think of going to school. Not me! . . . My children, well, who knows?" she shrugged her shoulders.

"You should think about it. You're pretty smart, and you have a very nice disposition."

"Oh, I know why," she grinned. "It's because I have an American name."

"Hey, I always wondered about that. What does Westi mean?"

Westi closed the door laughing. She wouldn't tell anyone that her mother had named her after a Westinghouse refrigerator!

* * *

It was past three in the afternoon when Westi finished at Lenny's. Even though she had worked all day, it seemed like Sunday. She was so happy; certainly, something good would happen at the bingo game.

"Mamá, I'm hungry," Susan said as they were walking down the street.

"Didn't you save a piece of bread from your breakfast?" The child nodded. "Well, now share it with your sister. You'll have to wait until dinner if you want anything else. We can't go around wasting food like that. We don't have enough for that, Susan."

Westi was afraid that she might have sounded too harsh to her five-year-old daughter and stopped to kiss her on the head. The dry piece of bread didn't look appetizing at all; just the same, Susan stopped for a moment to cut it between her hands.

"Wait, wait for me," she yelled when she was done. Her mother and younger sister were already about ten steps ahead of her.

"Westi!" A voice coming from one of the houses stopped them. "Come here a minute, please."

"Sure, Doña," Westi picked up her youngest daughter and walked toward the lady who called her.

"Oh, Westi, I need a favor from you. There's no one around to help me right now . . ."

"Sure, Doñita, what's the matter?"

"I was supposed to send a dress to Doña Sol today. I worked all night last night, and it's finished. But I don't feel well; my husband and my son aren't here to help me, and I'm afraid that I won't be able to take this dress to Doña Sol."

"Do you want me to do it for you?" Westi offered.

"Oh yes, Westi, I'll pay for your bus fare and give you one peso for the favor. You can leave your daughters with me so you can go faster. You don't know how much I'll appreciate it!"

Westi nodded. The seamstress went inside the house to wrap the dress and find the money to give to Westi.

"Where does Doña Sol live?"

"It's not too far by bus. Here's the address. You'll be there in five minutes after you take the bus at the rotunda."

Westi almost ran to the bus stop. She knew she had plenty of time, but the thought of her missing the game obsessed her. What if she lost the five dollars along the way? Immediately she touched the bill she had wrapped in an old handkerchief. What if her husband returned all of a sudden and took away from her the only extra money she had? The thought sent her running even faster down the block.

As soon as Westi got to Doña Sol's, the old woman asked her in and immediately took the dress out of the box to admire it.

"You know . . . what's your name?"

"Westi."

The old woman looked at her confused.

"Westi?"

"Yes, ma'am."

"Well, Westi, I always like to wear a new dress to the bingo game. It's the only time I ever go out during the week. It's worth it, though. Have you ever been there?"

Westi managed to gather all the courage she had and asked the stranger: "Do you know how to play well?" She hoped she wasn't doing the wrong thing by asking. "You know, who gets to win and how."

"Oh, it's not so easy," the old woman laughed. "I've done it myself a couple of times — win the grand prize, I mean — but it's just a matter of luck, you see . . ."

Westi couldn't have found a more likable topic for Doña Sol. When the young maid went back home, there was nothing she didn't know about the bingo game.

* * *

"Thirty-three, twenty-six, four, forty-five, sixty-six." At eight o'clock that night, Westi and her six children were walking to the bingo game. Susan and Cheli held each of her hands; Pico and Carlitos, the younger boys, held her wrists. José and Fernán, her oldest sons, walked in front of her, they claimed, to lead the way through the dark streets.

"Why is everything so dark, Mamá?" Cheli seldom spoke, but the darkness invariably scared her.

"The lights went out, silly, can't you see?" answered Pico.

The little girl just said "Oh" and tightened her grip on her mother's hand.

"Eleven, fifteen, fifty-eight, seventy," Westi's resolute step gave her children confidence. She looked as magnificent as her economic condition would allow. She had used talcum powder on her neck and shoulders, as she only did on very special occasions. The light yellow dress she was so proud of enveloped her shapely breasts and hips. Her full skirt gently brushed her strong, worker's legs with a rhythm all its own. She knew that her work sandals didn't do much to help her appearance; when she put them on earlier that evening, she had instinctively touched the five dollars she had wrapped in an old handkerchief. After all, that was the only thing she really needed to get in and win the game.

"Ten, thirty-three, twenty-six, forty-five, sixty-six," she repeated the numbes out loud, matching them to the count of every step they took.

"Mamá, what are you saying?" Susan, as usual, asked the questions. "We're going to buy another bed with those numbers, right?"

"I hope so, darling."

"But, Ma, you can't buy beds with numbers . . . What's a bingo?"

"Now, José, no questions. Mamá is the boss around here and you just do what she says." Westi had to stop her count in order to set her oldest son straight.

"It's the Virgin Mary, José, she's the one that's going to help us." Susan was an echo of her mother's words. The little boy didn't seem convinced, but he shrugged his shoulders and joined in the count his brothers and sisters were helping their mother keep.

"Eleven," Westi said.

"Eleven," the six children chorused.

"Fifteen," she added.

"Fifteen," they repeated again.

When they reached the steps of the Spanish Society of San Pedro de Macoris, the lights had come back, and Westi was grateful she had arrived on time.

The room was full of wooden chairs and rectangular wooden tables. Two huge crepe paper fans decorated each side of the door. Westi saw them and felt like running back home. It was no use procrastinating, and she got down on her knees and asked her children to gather around her. They looked confused and unaware of what was really going on.

"Now, children," she began. Her forehead and upper lip were wet with perspiration; the hands with which she touched Pico and Cheli were cold and quivering. "You can't go in with me now. Everyone who goes in there has to pay, and I only have enough money for my own way. I want you here all together in this window right here, where I can see you. Don't shout or scream at one another. Susan, take Cheli by the hand and don't let her go no matter what. Pico, take care of Carlitos. José and Fernán, take care of your younger brothers and sisters, you hear? If I have to walk out and take care of you, then I'll miss the numbers and I'll never win the money to buy us another bed.

"Mamá, why were you calling those numbers out loud?"

"They're the numbers that Doña Sol told me I would need to win the game tonight."

"Who's Doña Sol?"

"Not now, Susan, later. When we walk home, then we can talk. Right, honey?"

The little girl let go of her sister's hand to hug her mother affectionately. Moments later, Westi walked to the front entrance feeling like a black Saint Joan ready to be burned at the stake.

Right at the door, she unwrapped the bill she had been guarding all day. She gave it to the man in charge of the tickets, and when she saw it was no longer her own, she felt a void in the pit of her stomach.

Enough of that nonsense. Westi knew what she had to win; her solemn look turned into a laughing glance, and her nervous lips formed a smile.

Her first step was finding the card she would use the rest of the evening. Doña Sol had told her to be very careful and pick one with the right numbers. That's why Westi had tried to remember them on her way to the game. Thirty-three, twenty-six, four, forty-five. None of the cards had all the numbers she wanted! Westi, don't panic. Finally, she saw one with three of the numbers in a row: eleven, fifteen and four. That one would have to do.

The room was almost full by then. It seemed that most of the people who played were regulars at the game and really knew how to go about the preliminaries. Westi had to find a place to sit. "Oh, Holy Virgin, where?" she asked herself looking around.

"Westi, is it? Are you looking for someone?" Doña Sol's voice interrupted Westi's thoughts.

"No, ma'am, this is my first time, you see, and I don't know anyone. Where can I sit!" she asked in confusion.

"Anywhere you can find a place." Doña Sol stopped and thought for a moment. "There's an empty space at our table. You could sit with us if you want."

"Oh no, ma'am, I could never do that," Westi answered, embarrassed.

"If I tell you that you can, you can, Westi. Come with me." The old woman took her by the arm, and Westi had no choice but to follow.

Sol Aguado, 82, was an expert gambler, and so were the five ladies who shared her table every Wednesday. Their passion for the game was such that they brought their own set of chips to play among themselves before the actual game got started. In the preliminary games they bet dimes, so the amount they could win was not even that important. It was the thrill of it that made it all worthwhile.

"You'd better be careful tonight, ladies, I am not only lucky for the practice game, I'm winning the grand prize this evening. Just watch." Doña Emilia sounded so sure of herself that Westi felt weak and cold from fear. What if she lost her five dollars and didn't win any money . . . Momentarily she wondered whether or not she had made a mistake in coming.

"This must really matter to you," Doña Sol observed. "Why did you just cross yourself?"

"Oh, Doña Sol, I don't really know how to play this game and I've already given the man my five pesos. There's no backing out now, is there?"

"No, dear," she whispered. The game was about to start. The master of ceremonies was explaining the rules of the game, and Doña Sol asked again, "Why are you here today? I come to enjoy myself, you know, for pleasure. But you're much too concerned to be here just for fun."

"I've never been to a bingo game. Someone told me how, if I put in five pesos, I could win thirty, or an awful lot more. My children and I need another bed, and I can't seem to be able to find the money for it. I thought of the bingo game and . . ." She shrugged her shoulders helplessly. "I've been saving for two months to come here, and now I see how hard it is to win. I think I should have kept my five pesos and bought some food for my children, that's what I should have done!"

"First game of thirty dollars, starting with the first chip," the announcer's voice interrupted their conversation.

"Doña Sol smiled and whispered, "Don't worry!"

With each new game, the excitement increased. People were very quiet as the numbers were called; then, right after, they clapped, screamed funny remarks or moaned. Only the very poor had one card. Most players had more than three to try their luck.

During the first hour, Westi didn't win anything. At one point, she almost won; she filled every number space except one. Her heart throbbed violently; she sweat profusely; her hands were cold and trembling. Seventy-five dollars was the prize, and that was almost enough for a bed. If she couldn't buy a full bed, perhaps she could buy a smaller one and let some of the children sleep on the mattress and some on the box-spring. At least they could stretch out and . . .

"Sixty-three," the announcer called out.

Westi thought she would faint; someone else yelled: "Bingo!"

At ten fifteen, her only chance was the full card: one-hundred and fifty pesos, the best and last prize of the evening. Westi saw Lenny waving at her from the other side of the room; he shook his head to let her know that he hadn't won anything yet. Westi shook hers too; her sad smile and drooping eyebrows showed that she had lost all hope of ever winning. The announcer called a five minute recess before the longest game of the evening began.

The crowd became restless; people stood up to buy snacks and greet friends. At Westi's table, the furor had doubled. The old women were discussing why and how they had failed to win . . . so far! Doña Sol didn't say much; she looked at Westi and made it clear with her glance that she was tired of listening to her friends brag about their luck and expertise.

"Could I still win, Doña Sol?" Westi sounded depressed and worried.

"Anyone can still win, dear. It just takes luck."

"But I haven't even made it in the easy tries."

"You haven't been lucky yet, that's all. It's happened to me many times," the understanding lady explained. Westi's stooped shoulders showed that she had little energy or hope left. "Of course," Doña Sol continued, "I have never played to win money for something I needed badly."

"That makes the game very different. Ay, Doña Sol, every time someone yells 'bingo' I feel as if my soul were running away somewhere and leaving my body sitting here. I didn't think it was going to be like this." She shook her head. "I don't think that I can sit here and watch someone yell 'bingo' and win the money I need for our bed. I think I'm leaving! I would rather go and think that I could have won it. I don't ever want to lose this last game!" Westi stood up.

"Doing that won't even give you your five pesos back," the old woman warned. Westi sat down. "If you stay, at least you'll have a chance."

Westi glanced toward the window where her children were waiting. Cheli had found enough space on the old ledge to lie down and fall asleep. Susan was making sure that her younger sister didn't fall; when she saw her mother look in their direction, she waved back joyfully.

"Is that your daughter?" Doña Sol asked.

"Yes, one of them. My other daughter is sleeping right next to her, can you see them?" Westi pointed.

"How many more did you say you have?"

"Four boys."

Doña Sol's thoughtful stare was interrupted by the announcer's voice calling the people back to their seats to resume the game.

"Of course," she whispered to Westi, "sometimes we can even make luck move in our direction, if we give it a little push."

Westi sighed, wishing she knew how.

The sound of the numbers flooded the room. People smiled when their numbers were called out; some groaned when the little squares in their cards remained blank. Some of the more excitable players yelled: "Keep going! You're on the right track, buddy!" Others smiled furtively and covered the blank spaces on their cards with quick determination.

The bursts of emotion from the players around her made Westi's heart beat out of control. She admitted to herself that it had been the luckiest game she had played all evening. At least three of the five numbers in each column were full from the beginning. Slowly, others began to appear: fifty-seven, thirty-two, fifteen . . .

Westi only looked up when she realized she had only two more numbers left to win: twenty-two and four. Several minutes passed and her number was still not called. Her hand on her forehead, her elbow on the table, Westi could only see the nearly full card.

"Someone is going to yell 'bingo,' any time now," Doña Emilia said.

Westi felt like crying and hoped that no one would notice. As soon as she heard someone yell "bingo" she would stand up quietly and go home. Yes, she would take her children and never again would she return to a place that had made her totally miserable and had cost her five pesos. How could she have been so naive? How could she have imagined that anyone could get money that easily? She was twenty-two years old and still acted like a child. Why, all those people she had told about the bingo game probably laughed at her so hard that . . .

"Four," the announcer called.

Just when Westi was going to cover one of the two numbers she needed to win, she saw a hand take her card and put another one in its place. It was Doña Sol; she moved surreptitiously. Everyone else at the table was so absorbed by their own possibility of winning that Doña Sol's move remained a secret.

"Please, yell 'bingo,' Westi," Doña Sol whispered.

"She won?" Doña Emilia interrupted.

"Who won?" someone else asked.

"Westi," Doña Sol answered, pointing to the girl sitting beside her. "Bingo! Bingo! Stop the game, we have a winner!" Doña Sol's voice always trembled a little when she screamed, but she managed to get the announcer's attention, stop the game and make Westi walk to the front table with the winning card in her hand.

III. BAD VIBES

Presagio

Eliana Rivero

Cuando sueño que tu sangre se vierte,
que te matan en la avenida de mi casa,
se apodera de mí
la indecente nostalgia de tu cuerpo
como una araña cenicienta
Veo tu rostro blanco,
tus piernas sin camino,
tu lengua inmóvil como en el silencio
Y pienso que es imposible que te mueras,
que te persigan hasta mi interior

Pero hay calles ascendentes de piedra,
como en Santiago,
puentes visibles a la luz de faroles,
jardín de noche con magnolias abiertas
En un momento indefinido,
algo se oye
Pasos
se precipitan desde el tramo angular,
resuenan entre otros
Los reconozco;
se me pierden
Ni siquiera te defienden mis brazos
cuando las bestias te acorralan
Te veo
rodar enrojecido,
sudar el frío de la muerte,
derribarte como un pistilo destrozado

Y no puedo resucitar del sueño,
reírme del verdugo sureño y de sus manos,
prevenirle
que el hacha con que te destruye
desaparecerá al amanecer
Y sigues

detenido en tu luna de jacintos:
tu peso
es un ancla de hielo entre los hombros

La suicida

Marjorie Agosín

Entre las piedras,
desnuda entre los vestigios,
con la boca entre dormida
y abierta,
con los brazos apresurados
para el des-amor
ella,
se vuelve hermosa
mientras la vemos
simple, extinguida,
como la noche misma.
Ella,
la suicida
que surge ante los transeúntes
en una inmensa plenitud
en una pregunta mentirosa
¿Por qué tiene olor a muerte?
¿a culebras destrenzadas?

¿Por qué se fue?

Ella nos mira,
y cada vez se vuelve más hermosa.
porque es ajena
y desciende en un círculo
alrededor de sus manos
que no desean,
de su piel con fragancias y
crisantemos.

Ella, la suicida,
ardiendo entre las piedras,
sumergida entre las aguas,
haciendo de la
noche
un secreto
y de la vida
nada más
que una mujer extendida entre las piedras ardiendo
oyéndose
en nuestra ausencia.

Yo la miro
y es cada visión más hermosa.

The Other

Judith Ortiz Cofer

A sloe-eyed dark woman shadows me.
In the morning she sings
Spanish love songs in a high
falsetto filling my shower stall
with echoes.
She is by my side
in front of the mirror as I slip
into my tailored skirt and she
into her red cotton dress.
She shakes out her black mane as I
run a comb through my close-cropped cap.
Her mouth is like a red bull's eye
daring me.
Everywhere I go I must
make room for her: she crowds me
in elevators where others wonder
at all the space I need.
At night her weight tips my bed, and
it is her wild dreams that run rampant
through my head exhausting me. Her heartbeats,
like dozens of spiders carrying the poison
of her restlessness over the small
distance that separates us,
drag their countless legs
over my bare flesh.

The Escape

Achy Obejas

The day was nearly finished, falling from the horizon in bold streaks of red and yellow: high tide, eating away at the shore, then pushing back the sandy crumbs.

Nina would have to wait now, fingers tightly gripping the inflated yellow raft. With each pull and tug of the waves, she saw the purple and beige shadows straining in the malignant suds. Seconds later the curl would snap on the shore and spray the grainy, pebbled sand.

For a moment she could feel the water on her face, could lick the sharp taste on her lips.

She knew she would never make it out with the sea in such an uproar. Some bronzed muscleboy with official green trunks would stop her as soon as she dropped into the foam. He would rush in and pull her out, his arm tight around her neck.

Nina half imagined she could die right there, her body serving as the object of a tug of war between the lifeguard and the currents. The muscles of his arm would tighten like a vise, cutting into her breathing until it stopped its rhythm.

He would never know he had killed her but would assume, would need to assume, that she was already gone when he reached her. He would believe himself a hero, even if a tragic one. He would say, "I did all I could. I pulled her to the shore. I gave her mouth-to-mouth resuscitation. I tried to revive her every way I know how."

The crowd that always gathers in macabre curiosity at such events would remember that there was no blood or excrement. It would only retain the romantic portrait of the young man in official green trunks leaning over her body. It would never suspect him.

She knew that entering the water now would result in this, not in a dignified death. The end would only be the nervous clutching steel arm of a muscleboy in official green trunks.

And Nina couldn't stand for that.

It would be another hour or two, or maybe longer, before she could begin. Spying the corner of a newspaper page peeking out of the sand, she wondered whether the weather report might not accurately forecast the fall of the tide.

But to get the day's edition, she had to leave the shore, shuffle to the seawalk, go through the park, cross the street, and find a newstand still open. It seemed more of an effort than she was willing to make.

In a single motion, she crossed her legs and lowered her body to the sand. It was one of those casual expressions of youth, a demonstration of the swiftness and equilibrium that is only associated with the teen years.

She tossed her hair back. It was meant as part of a grander pose, but the wind defied her, bringing the strands around so that the ends stung and bit at her face. With a spark of temporary anger, she pulled the hair back its full length and tied it behind her with the rubber band that had served as company to the sturdy gold bracelet on her wrist.

The bracelet, a present from her father, did not bear her name, nor his. It was more an expression of his limitless hopes for her. On the bracelet's now slightly worn surface, in a delicate and traditional script, was written one word: immortal.

Nina found it ironic even when she received it, at a birthday party in a friend's huge house in north Miami Beach. It must have been a birthday present, but she couldn't be sure. What was certain was that he had given it to her.

Her memories were gauzed, so the scene of her father in a white guayabera, with its four embroidered pockets and his slicked-back hair, lost all its detail. The party faces looked on, most as confused as hers but feeling the obligation to express wonder at the father's gift to the daughter. They were soft smiles and forced sighs.

Immortal: it seemed inappropriate. It had something to do with living. And dying. Or rather, with not dying. She thought it perverse.

She had never liked the bracelet. Instead of giving her strength as intended, it had only caused her to feel guilty, burdened. Its presence on her wrist drew more discussion than she had ever wanted — "What does it mean?" "Who gave it to you?"

Nina wore the bracelet out of obligation. She knew that leaving it on her bureau would strike her father as cold. She could see his features shrinking on his face, his eyes avoiding her at dinner.

But the bracelet was useless. What she wanted was death. There would be no need for inspiration, for immortality. Other than to rub the irony in his face, there would be no reason to keep it.

She had started to finger the lock when she heard the lifeguard give the signal, making it safe to go back to the water. In his official green trunks, he waved a pair of multi-colored flags. Squinting in the harsh white light creeping through the parting clouds, she saw him as an insignificant yellow, brown, and green smear against the pink sand.

She placed the raft in the choppy water. Instantly her denim shorts darkened and the white T-shirt became transparent, revealing an orange and yellow pattern against her breasts. She threw herself on the raft, stroking the water with each arm and feeling the currents under her weight.

It would take a long time to go where she wanted to go. It would take hours, maybe days. So far it had been a lifetime.

She felt courageous, smooth, slightly cruel. She felt her muscles tense and release and was proud of the way her biceps swelled when she dug through the suds. When the water slapped her face, she opened her mouth and let the salt caress her tongue and gums, then let it dribble from the corners and run down her neck. She felt the streams like new veins. She thought she knew what she looked like, picturing an Olympic swimmer on a color television screen coming up for air.

Nina shifted her weight, anticipating each pull and shove, closed her eyes, and turned her head seconds before a wet hand crossed her features. She advanced against each ramming wave with almost equal verve. She felt the pain and it was fine.

Soon the head-on attack ceased. The water had mounds that shifted darkly under the glaring yellow raft. She was being carried along, an undercurrent pulling her out. She stopped struggling, closed her eyes, and held on tightly. Her arms relaxed, with no cramps, after a minute or two.

Above her the sky was now navy blue with wisps of grey. She heard small splashes as little waves attempted to gain momentum around her, then puttered out. Most of all, she heard a hum, a low deep hum that seemed to come from everywhere.

She was not afraid.

But suddenly she was not on the raft, not feeling the warm breeze against her legs, not feeling the skin between air and sea. Her clothes seemed heavy; they had a life of their own, loosely falling around her, pulling her up, down, to the sides with gentle tugs.

She was floating, far away, very close, warm and cold; she was embraced, covered, protected. She was touched everywhere, from the inside of her earlobes to the places between her skin and the heavy denim.

Nina thrust her arms out and felt nothing. She stretched her legs, feeling the sensations of the movement itself, but movement only as if through syrup. There was a thick weight on her temple; the heavy hum turned into a screech.

She opened her eyes, immediately feeling the salt sting: the shadows, the haze; she felt a hand at her throat, at her lungs. Her own hand reached up and shot from under the water, grasping nothing but air—suddenly tangible, concrete.

Her muscles in a knot, she struggled to the surface, each step disappearing from under her. This time when the water ran through her mouth she pictured the last scene from *Moby Dick*, with the sailor wrapped around a plank of wood, desperate and fearful. It was a wide scene, black and white, impossible to believe, yet so real.

But she didn't have a plank of wood. Her raft was gone, pulled from under her. She kicked and thrust her weight past the surface, turning, hoping to find it. When she fell once more, she felt a grazing against her foot, a slick silver something shaving past her tight pale flesh. She was afraid, afraid.

It invaded her throat, then exploded in words—"Oh my God!" "My God, help me!" "Help!"— but there was no God, no help, only navy blue skies, grey clouds, and white lines that looked like saliva in the sickly green water. Her sounds were distant and solitary. She felt them echo, dwarfed by the vastness of the ocean.

Nina splashed, thrashed about, submerged against her will, lost control of her muscles, of the pain that had electrified her right arm in an instant. She took air in large gulps, spit water, swallowed blood from seared lips. When her bracelet caught the T-shirt, it tore it unexpectedly. The bathing suit cupping her breasts was straining her lungs, suffocating her.

She started to feel her task was accomplished, that she would die, drown, fulfill her deathwish. The official report would call it accidental, never suicide. She suddenly comprehended how unsure she was of either description's accuracy.

And then she felt the tapping at her shoulder, almost as if on a dance floor. Someone, something, wanted to interrupt, but for an instant she was afraid to look, afraid of the new partner, of the supernatural, the spiritual. (Had she crossed over already? Had she died? When? In what instant? What caused it? What was she doing when it happened?)

Bobbing in the water, looking like an animated Disney character, the yellow raft edged off the water, unable to conform its ribbed flat shape to the changing, slithering surface.

Nina grabbed the raft so hard and so fast she was afraid she had ruptured it. She heaved her body, now torturously heavy, onto it and breathed relief in long rapid succession. She felt her breath against the canvas, soaking through the fabric.

She rested. She opened and closed her eyes, feeling the redness inked in them by the salt. It seemed a long time. She reached behind her and undid her bathing suit top. With a minimum of effort, she pulled it off and left her torn T-shirt against against her breasts. Everything felt lighter. She turned herself around on the raft and faced the sky.

Nina wondered, with her chafed lips in motion, if any of what had just happened to her had been the same for the little American girl.

She couldn't remember the girl's name, only that she was American, with lifeless reddish-blond hair and hazel eyes. The little girl sported a smattering of freckles around her nose and almost blond eyelashes that seemed fuzzy and alien. She had blue-veined pink cheeks.

Nina met her in 1964, when they were both seven years old. Nina's father, still handsome in his late thirties, had invited the little girl and her father, a paunchy red-cheeked American of a man, for a final ride on the boat that had brought Nina's family from Cuba to Florida.

Nina's younger brother, a bespectacled four-year old with little motor coordination, had been invited along at the last minute. The brother, with the legs of his glasses extended by an elastic strap around his head, cowered in the car duing the ride to the port. He did not look forward to reliving any recent memories.

He had spent the trip from Cuba in a state of seasickness and fear. His little hands had gripped Nina's sweater at the beginning of the journey and hadn't unlocked until an American sailor gently pried them off. He had cried quietly on her shoulder, had vomited on Nina's thighs. Yet she had held him, never telling anyone of his shivering from fright.

The boat they journeyed in was a muddy red, 28 feet long, and the carrier of almost fifty passengers on its trip through international waters. It had been stolen from a tropical harbor after days of desperate planning. When its mission was accomplished, the United States government set it to rest off a Miami port. It slept on the rim of the water, collecting barnacles and green moss on its sides. Empty, the little vessel grew old, worn, and in desperate need of attention.

A decision was finally made. It would be destroyed. When notified, her father allowed fat tears to form on the edges of his eyes. With a sense of destiny, he decided to take a final ride in the boat. Permission from the State Department came quickly and the previously classified location of the boat was revealed.

For the occasion, Nina's father wore grey work pants and a light green shirt of synthetic material. A white undershirt left tracks around his arms and clavicles. A glass case, pens, and a miniature ruler protruded from his shirt pocket. He didn't notice the ink stains, like light blue spiders, near the seams. The American, much older than he, wore similar dress, only his shirt was of natural fiber and fit him snugly. He also wore a sailor's cap, slightly cocked and spotless.

His daughter was dressed in clean white and blue cotton, a ribbon photographically tied in her hair. Nina was not as picture perfect: A permanently sad expression widened her dark watery eyes; she was thin and spidery, with faded orange skin. (In a few years, the nearly sunless existence of life in the northern regions of the United States would render her a pale yellow, an imperfect white.) She wore the same faded sweater she had worn on the escape from Cuba. Under it was a dull plaid dress given her by the volunteers at Freedom House, or what her family called "El Refugio."

When the two girls met, the fathers gloated: "Such pretty girls." But Nina soon felt her father's uneasiness, his awareness of her simple appearance, the signs of charity of the ill-fitting dress. Even as he stretched his lips to smile, she could see the shame and pity in his liquid eyes. In a moment, with a hand gesture understood by all, he suggested that she brush her hair or tie it back. She nodded, and did nothing.

Neither man noticed. Or perhaps they pretended not to notice. The little American girl, however, noticed enough to remind her at least twice. Nina ignored her. The brother, in a silent conspiracy, stayed close to Nina.

The ride began without incident. The five climbed into the boat, with both adults at the helm. At first the children tried to look ahead, over the nose of the boat and into the horizon. But they were little and soon tired of leaning on their toes and holding on to each other and their fathers.

After a few minutes, the view seemed the same. The Miami skyline had shrunk dramatically on the edge of the sea, but it had quickly become a matter of degree. They had not noticed the changes in the ocean, the rich blues and blacks as they reached deeper waters. Nothing matched the first few minutes, when they shot from the shore, holding firmly against the wind.

When the kids tired, they shrunk toward the back of the boat, where Nina quickly discovered the sudsy ridges formed by the boat slicing through the sea. She looked into the distance and noticed that the lines were drawn in the ocean for a great many miles. Maybe, she thought, they went below the surface and lasted forever. It interested her, but less because of the pattern than because it gave her an excuse for solitude.

The American girl, having wandered close, nudged Nina and pointed to the wisps of hair that jerked about in the wind. She motioned that it be tied back, then crossed her arms together, waiting. But Nina liked her hair the way it was, dancing around her head, free from restraint. She did not like the other girl's ribbon; she did not like the feminine dress that made both her father and her so nervous, unsure.

When the girl spoke, Nina did not understand her. Worse, she hardly heard her above the noise of the boat. What she saw was an American mouth moving in disjointed fashion, tongue and lips forming patterns which, like the boat on the water, intrigued her but made no sense.

The little girl sighed as if exasperated. She spoke again, pointed at Nina and giggled into her child-palm. Nina approached her cautiously because of the constant movement of the boat and stood firmly in front of her.

The little girl registered the menace and without a trace of laughter, spoke again. Then she crossed her arms, shrugged her shoulders, and painted a bored, disdainful expression across her features. Nina raised both hands and with one quick gesture pushed the girl off the boat and into the white lines in the water.

The brother immediately felt around his head to make sure the straps to his glasses were still in place. The little girl, like the skyline, had shrunk instantly. She was now a thrashing blot becoming more and more distant in the water. He caught Nina's eye. She said nothing, but brought her hand to her mouth and touched her lip.

He didn't hesitate but turned to the men, grabbed his father by the leg of his trousers, and screamed above the noise: "She fell in the water! She fell in the water!" His finger pointed in the direction of the lump in the sea.

The men gasped, frantically turned the boat around, and rushed to the American's daughter. Nina remained silent, but looked ahead, wondering how they would slow down when they reached her, afraid they would hit her by accident. But she didn't wonder long. In a minute her father was stripped to the waist and diving into the water. The glass case and pens spilled onto the floor of the vessel, the blue spiders on the shirt pocket bloated out of shape by contact with wetness. The American screamed. By the time Nina's father brought the little girl to the boat, she was a lifeless doll, and the big, brawny American was reduced to a heaving hulk bent over her body.

Seven years later Nina remembered the episode while floating on her back on the yellow raft. She remembered the funeral, her first, and the doll-like cheeks on the little girl. She had not cried, unable to bring tears to her eyes, unable to bridge the distance between herself and the yellow curls resting on the white silk of the coffin.

The tears had come later: when she secretly flushed dinner down the toilet, horrible refugee cornmeal dinners from Freedom House; when her father, in a drunken stupor, cried about his lost Cuba—his own personal Cuba—and pounded his frustrations on her mother's shoulders and back; when a boy with white eyelashes cupped her girlish breast with his hand under the First Street pier in Miami Beach; when her brother, protected by a silent covenant, lifted hard-earned dollars from their mother's purse in Nina's full view.

Now, with the sky above her growing darker and a cracking sound erupting from behind black clouds, Nina examined her motives for death—her debt to the American, to the ocean, to God. She would free her family—a life for a life—so that the days could once more be sunny and snowless and the afternoon could be spent feeding the pigeons along the Malecón.

Maybe her body would wash up in Cuba, with flesh hanging from the bones and her clothes rotting. Would they bury her? Would they, thinking she was an American, feed her to the animals? Would they hang her in the plaza to show the fate of the refugees?

Thunder rattled her. She sat up on the raft, bringing her arms quickly in front of her. She felt her bracelet snag on the raft's mouthpiece and snap, slipping from her wrist and over the side. When she reached down to grab it, she heard a hiss, almost a jeer. She felt around to find the escape of air but had no immediate success. She leaned down, a little desperate now, and used both her hands in her search. The raft under her softened. Above, the sky was getting uglier. Looking around her, Nina felt a sudden terror: The night had begun, the city's skyline had fallen from view, and bold streaks of ominous colors covered the flat horizon.

IV. SAGE

El lugar de la mujer

Miriam Bornstein

Jung diría que pertenezco a la luna
(tengo estos poemas para comprobarlo)
pero me estoy dejando crecer las uñas
por si acaso se equivoca.

The Rose

Diana Rivera

I found a rose in the streets
of Chinatown, by crates of peas and
pomegranates, two petals about to fall
in the cold night, but it was complete.

After days of abstinence,
blue veins opened in the bathtub,
reading psychotic terms
I found the rose that saved me.

It was a miracle! Who, nowadays,
finds a rose on the sidewalk,
in the night over the shadows,
who finds a rose?

I found a rose, scarlet and bright,
with the most enormous thorns I have
yet seen, and the longest stem,
after my longest period of hibernation.

I found a rose in winter,
before the snow fell and buried it
and I buried myself,
I found it.

And the Chinese man said:
"For your lover!"
But the night asked me, desperately,
to clench to it with both hands.

Lo que somos

Marjorie Agosín

El amor deja de ser lo de antes,
compréndanme, no hay para qué
hacerse la dormida
entre corpiño y camisón
ni inventar a un pene
despegando en
la oscuridad de la
cripta conyugal

Ya no somos tan épicas
mas forniconas, iconoclastas
un poco señoras deseosas de
un buen pasar, como los muchachos por cierto
con un coito liviano
después del almuerzo
y ya está.

Nueva versión del paraíso

Marjorie Agosín

Adán se cansó del escenario vacío
del cigarrillo en la boca
y pidió que le trajesen a la
Eva o a la María,
Dios sometido y cabizbajo
lo hizo soñar despierto
o soñó dormido
le sacó una costilla dorada
como espejo
la amasó como tortilla española
redonda, fina, cebollenta

y colorín colorado
apareció Eva
a su lado.

La Eva tenía buena pinta
rubia, flaca
con olor de aguas
y se abanicaba lejana, desnuda
en una roca del paraíso.

Adán le pedía cosas,
brebajes,
favores de intercambio y entrepiernas
Eva hincada lavábale la ropa
en el Eufrates
le traía hierbas buenas
alquimias y algas
para la movediza garganta del Adán.

Eva cansada del Adán
que le decía
ven pa cá
límpiame el cabello
frota las piedras para huevos revueltos
entonces
ella decidió aliarse con la culebra
comiendo una manzanita
con forma de nalgas y agua bendita
Adán también un mordisco le plantó
y la huella de esa delicia
en la garganta para siempre se
le quedó

Dios escribió un libro gordísimo
para testimoniar de la manzana de Adán
que realmente era de Eva
pero Adán protagonizó el cuento
y la Eva un mero instrumento
entonces Dios se enfadó
acusó a Eva
de desobediencia
de moverse como serpiente
de activa pecadora transgresora
la culparon de los males de Adán
de su resfriado
de las sequías
huracanes
el flujo menstrual
los espejos cóncavos

Y Eva enmudeció
se amarró el cabello
sumisa obedeció
a los hijos de Adán y su manzana,
empezó a rezar
a engordar
era tan gorda como el libro que Dios seguía
    escribiendo
no dormía desnuda
compró un camisón de algodón paraíso
en los catálogos de las viejas gitanas
que viajaban por los cien años de soledad
Eva fue inmaculada
como Dios manda
concibió a los hijos de Adán
así no más
iban de pic-nic al santo sepulcro
y boom nacían los chiquillos
como arbustos silvestres en una selva virgen.

Eva dejó de beber Gin con Gin
en la orilla del Eufrates
comenzó a escribir un libro de recetas para el fuego
    perfecto
aunque nunca le hizo la competencia a Dios
finalmente se casó con Adán
él le cambió de nombre
y le dijo
ahora
esclava de mi carne
sirvienta de mis huesos

te llamarás mujer.

Tihuique (Now Let Us Go)

Gloria Anzaldúa

One year in a distant century during Teoteco,
the 12th month of the solar year, Five Rabbit,
in the reign of Four-Water Sun,
I carved 12,000 hearts
in honor of Huitzilopochtli, God of War,
who made the Sun rise each morning.

In each succeeding year thereafter
ceremonial drunkenness robbed me
for many hearts embraced the furnace sacrifice.
Only the hearts of the finest Nahuatl braves
and luckiest prisoners tasted me.
One year the priests and warriors
ate the sacred flesh.

Today I lie in a musty museum
and register 5.5 on Mohs' scale.
But my origin, volcanic obsidian,
hard as granite
comes in good stead.

In my childhood I was a mirror.
I threw a vitreous luster, dark-green.
But now the iron oxide running in my veins
dulls my edge
and the air bubbles trapped in me
reflect my age.
    Time passes.
    I rest and await the flesh.

Chant Number One

(These chants were inspired by the chants of
María Sabina, a visionary and a shaman, who
lives in the mountains of Oaxaca.)

Miriam de Uriarte

Because this is the summer of great happiness
Because my Chinese fortune cookie is always right
Because the doves laid three eggs
Because in my dreams I am the outhouse woman
Because the man at the window was like cold air on the back of my neck
Because all day we lived together
Because the White-Sided Pacific Dolphin had a friend, the seal
Because the Manatee eats lettuce underwater and doesn't drown
Because the fog comes in on casters
Because you are the old silver fox.

I am the jingling woman
I am the woman of the house
I am the dove woman
I am the woman of hammered tin
I am the Mexican woman
I am the woman of the dancing tongues
I am the half-say woman
word woman.

Chant Number Two

Miriam de Uriarte

Because I am a woman who has traveled
Because I travel again
Because I know when the earth under my feet is wet
Because I remember the smell of wet wood burning
Because I have seen the smoke curl in the morning mountains
Because I have lived on both sides of the mountain
Because I have awoken between white sheets
Because I have spoken your language
Because my words belong to different kinds of dark

I am the solitary woman
I am the woman of rains
I am the woman of blue smoke
I am the woman of mountain paths
I am the woman of white linen
I am the woman of broken words
Dark word woman.

Chant Number Three

Miriam de Uriarte

Because I woke up early
Because the shadows of morning are white
Because you are in the room
Because my house smells of jasmine
Because the shadows are cool before the traffic begins
Because the kitchen smells of sweet coffee
Because I remember the taste of honey rolls in the garden
Because there are moments I pause to whistle to the hummingbird
Because my legs don't hesitate two stairs at a time

I am the sun woman
I am the woman of the morning
I am the woman who breathes
I am the woman who dances
I am the woman who savors
I am the woman who sings in her sleep
I am the whistling woman
I am the woman who visits you
Hummingbird woman.

V. OPPRESSION

Pene

Marjorie Agosín

Y tanto se ha escrito sobre los senos
senos como colina
senos de agua
senos donde se hará la primavera
y ahora
lancémonos al pene
pene como arruga
pene como cabeza inclinada
pene haciendo la reverencia
ante la magia de una ranura.

Pene sacudido de orines
cansado de tanta salida y despedida
pene como una presa al horno
o una sopa de pollos pelados.

¿Y ahora entenderán por qué es tiempo
de cambiar el disco?

Penélope I

Marjorie Agosín

Oiga doña Penélope:
¿hasta cuándo teje
la bufanda para don Ulises?
el gorrito
para el Ulises,
los calcetines para el Ulises,
cuando dicen
que ni pasa frío
en los pies,
y que en el ancho mar
tiene con las sirenas
un buen pasar,

cuentan los mensajeros,
y uno que otro forastero,
que lo vieron descalzo cantar
con doña Circe,
en una extraña ciudad
y otros dicen que fue con la Eurídice
que lo vieron amainar,
y Ud. teje y desteje
las horas
de la soledad
la ausencia sin piedad.
Flaca y apolillá,
de tanto esperar sentá,
cuando el muy canallita
de la Itaca se ha olvidado
y de Ud. señora mía,
al condenao le gusta pensar
que Penélope la esposa fiel
lo espera sin cesar,
mientras que el otro por allá
no le hace el quite al
buen pasar,
oiga doña Penélope,
avívese,
y por lo menos venda
una bufandita.

Basurero nacional

(Para los mexicanos obligados a vivir
de los desperdicios de otros)

Miriam Bornstein

Como rey rodeado de tus escombros
lujos deshilachados
eufemismos de consumidores
ideas desalojadas y apestosas
cantatas, pinturas, novelas de Cabrera Infante
una buena dosis de Octavio Paz
y un poco de Miami:
        esto no te salva
          ni te ampara de los gases
               el humo en las entrañas.
La civilización no se extiende hasta llegar a ti
y así quedas reducido
               pulgarcito entre los despojos
               aún más poderosos que tu propio semen.
Tus hijos no bastan para sobrevivirte
               entre la prisa del tráfico
               y monumentos a los monumentos.
Sin embargo persistes en tu presencia.
La ciudad entera está sitiada por tu ejército de hambre
por tus vestiduras de lata y cartón
con un anuncio agotado donde sea.
Algún día perderán la lista de los perdidos
y los gestos del acero dejarán de asustarte.

Con el bote en la mano

Carolina Mata de Woodruff

Ella tenía unos ocho años por ahí, no me acuerdo muy bien. La cosa es que venía del Norte rumbo a Tejas. Acababan de venirse del tomate en Illinois y venía toda la familia muy contenta porque pos ya iban pa su casa y a la escuela.

La cosa pasó así: Hermila era una de nueve mujeres que había en su hogar, y la habían dejado en un garache sin querer. Dicen que se pararon en un garache a echar gas, y cuando no se iba a quedar, sí era de noche y no se veía, sí iban todos en la troca cuando se subieron pa seguir el camino.

Hermila se había bajado a tirar el bote donde iban pa fuera en la troca. Sólo lo usaban cuando no querían pararse pa no gastar mucho tiempo parándose. Primero, cuando entró al excusado, no podía abrir el bote. Tenía tapadera, como era uno de esos botes de manteca. ¡Hasta que al fin lo abrió! Ya toda su familia, sus cinco hermanos y sus ocho hermanas se habían subido en la troca y su mamá y su papá también.

En la troca don Chuy le preguntó a Berta que si todos ya estaban arriba. Ella contestó que sí. Como preguntó a los chiquillos y estaba oscuro, ella creyó que estaban todos en la troca. ¡No se dieron cuenta que habían dejado una criatura largada en la estación de gasolina!

Mientras tanto, Hermila en el garache ya había tirado las aguas que traiba el bote. Y cuando quiso abrir la puerta del excusado pa salirse, no pudo. ¡Qué desengaño para ella! Toda asustada le movía a la tranca a un lado y a otro. Y como quiera la puerta no se abría. En su mente parecía que ya había pasado una eternidad dentro de esas cuatro paredes. Al fin usó la cabeza y se salió por debajo gateando para poder pasar.

Dicen que cuando salió pa fuera, la troca ya se había ido y comenzó a correr hacia ella. Mientras tanto lloraba desesperadamente con el bote en la mano. El viejo del garache la divisó y corrió hacia ella. Se la trajo pal garache y la sentó en la máquina de sodas. Les llamó a los policías para ver si podían alcanzar la troca. Ya tenían más de veinte minutos de haberse ido por el freeway.

Mientras tanto, en la troca doña Berta había comprado unas galletitas para todos y comenzó a llamar todos los nombres. Cuando llegó al de Hermila, nadie contestaba. ¡Pos cómo iba a contestar, si la habían dejado largada!

Doña Berta y los muchachos cogieron algo para pegar sobre las paredes para que don Chuy los oyera. Se detuvo hasta que el policía le dijo que había dejado una chiquilla en el garache.

Otra familia de compañeros venía con don Chuy. Como manejaban una camioneta, a ellos los mandaron a que fueran a recoger a Hermila.

Cuando regresaron con Hermila, venía con una soda coka y unas galletitas de queso y con el bote en la mano. Todos comenzaron a reírse como si les pareciera curioso ver a la chiquilla con el bote en la mano. Dicen que el pueblo donde la dejaron era Little Rock, Arkansas. Sí, me parece que allí fue; cómo no me voy a acordar si yo iba también con ellos.

La despedida

Bárbara Mújica

Yo no sé exactamente lo que pasó. La verdad es que yo me llevaba bien con la señora. Era una mujer resimpática, bien tranquila. No sé por qué después las cosas se echaron a perder.

Empecé a trabajar en aquella casa hace como seis meses. Fue una tremenda suerte haber encontrado a la señora Carolyn porque no todo el mundo está dispuesto a tomar a una mujer como yo, con una guagua. La prueba es que desde entonces no trabajo, excepto los martes y los viernes, cuando le plancho a la alemana que vive en la Massachusetts Avenue.

La señora Carolyn me puso las cosas bien claras desde el principio. Trabajaba, me dijo, y necesitaba que alguien le hiciera el aseo y se ocupara del niño . . . Billy se llamaba . . . tenía dos años y era un amor de chicoco . . . La niña . . . se llamaba Pámela . . . no era problema porque estaba más grande e iba al colegio. Lo importante, me dijo la señora, era que yo estuviera allí temprano, a las ocho, porque ella no podía llegar tarde a la oficina. No le importaba que yo llevara a Bertito, me dijo, porque le serviría de compañero a su hijito. Me pagaba treinta y cinco dólares al día.

—Pide cuarenta —me dijo Alberto.

—No —le dije. —Con los treinta y cinco estoy bien. Después me subirá.

—La Chely gana cuarenta y dos.

—La Chely no anda acarreando una guagua mientras trabaja —le dije. —Además, ella habla bastante inglés. Puede trabajar en cualquier casa. La ventaja aquí es que la señora Carolyn sabe castellano.

—¿Ah sí? —me dijo. —¿Qué tal habla?

—Chapurrea no más.

—Ya.

Pero nos entendemos, y eso es lo principal. Otra cosa, Alberto, cuando una está aquí de ilegal, no puede pedir la luna.

—La Chely está aquí de ilegal. Todo el mundo está aquí de ilegal.

—Deja las cosas como están —le dije. —La señora Carolyn es rebuena persona. Me gusta.

—¿Y el tipo?

—¿Qué tipo?

—El, pu'. El marido de ella.

—¿Qué tiene?

—¿El anda en pelota mientras vos estái allí con el cabro?

—¿Estái loco? ¿Cómo se te ocurre?

Más tarde llamé a la señora Carolyn y le pregunté lo de la plata. Ella me dijo que por el momento no podía pagarme más. Me dijo que para ellos treinta y cinco dólares eran un montón, que su esposo le había dicho que era absurdo pagarle esa cantidad a una mujer que venía a trabajar con una guagua en brazos, pero que ella entendía mi situación porque también era una mujer con niños que tenía que trabajar.

—Se está aprovechando de vos —me dijo Alberto. —Igual te podría pagar los cuarenta.

—No entendí —le expliqué. Esta gente no es rica.

—No fueran ricos, no tomarían a una empleada.

—No es cierto, Alberto —le dije. —Ella me contó que con los dos trabajando apenas les alcanzaba la plata para pagar la renta.

La verdad es que la mujer me daba pena. Entre el trabajo y los niños y el marido, andaba medio vuelta loca. Era secretaria o algo así. Trabajaba en una empresa donde escribía a máquina y llevaba las cuentas.

—Mire, Rosa —me dijo un día la señora Carolyn. Mi marido está quejándose. No le gusta que venga con el bebé. Le dije que el niño no molesta, que usted lo deja en la andadera todo el día, pero él dice que más adelante, cuando empiece a caminar, va a destruirle todos los juguetes a Billy.

—No es cierto, señora —le dije. —Tendré mucho cuidado.

—Mire —me dijo. Sería tal vez más conveniente que usted llegara a las ocho y cuarto. Mi marido parte a las ocho . . . o a veces aún más temprano. Así no la vería . . . digo . . . no se ofenda, Rosa . . . lo único que quiero yo es evitar un conflicto. Ya sabe que a usted la estimo mucho . . . y la necesito.

—Sí, señora —le dije. —Entiendo.

—Pero no llegue después de las ocho y cuarto —me dijo. —Porque yo no puedo llegar tarde a la oficina. Y antes de ir a trabajar tengo que llevar a la Pámela al colegio.

A Alberto le pareció rebién el arreglo. —Ya que no tení que estar allí tan temprano —me dijo —podí llevarme a mí al trabajo.

—No voy a alcanzar . . .

—Demás alcanzái. ¿A vos te parece justo que tengamos un solo auto y siempre te lo lleví vos? Ten un poco de consideración, por favor, Rosa. Estoy harto ya de tomar el micro.

Alberto trabaja de portero en un edificio que está en la Connecticut Avenue. Es un solo bus . . . el L2 . . . no es complicado . . . pero para evitar boches prometí dejarlo a él antes de ir a Bethesda, donde vive la señora Carolyn.

La primera vez que hice esa maroma me enredé bastante y no llegué al trabajo hasta un cuarto para las nueve. A la señora Carolyn la encontré en lágrimas.

—Pensaba que usted ya no venía —me dijo.

Me lancé a darle una explicación pero ella estaba demasiado trastornada para escucharme. Agarró a la Pámela y salió corriendo.

Al día siguiente también llegué tarde, esta vez porque Alberto se demoró en vestirse y en desayunar. Ella no dijo nada pero vi que estaba muy molesta. Al volver de la oficina entró a la cocina donde yo estaba dándole de comer a Bertito.

—Rosa —me dijo. —Usted sabe que yo no puedo permitir que usted aparezca a un cuarto para las nueve. Dos días seguidos he llegado tarde a la oficina. Esto no puede seguir. Me van a echar. Yo le expliqué cuál era mi situación cuando la tomé.

Alberto se puso furioso cuando le dije que ya no iba a poder llevarlo al trabajo.

—Vos soi una gran egoísta —me gritó.

—¿Qué querí que te diga? —le contesté. —La patrona dice que tengo que llegar temprano. Si te parece bien, te llevo a las siete y media. Así estoy donde ella a las ocho y cuarto.

—Muy temprano para mí.

—Pues, mala pata. No son tantas las opciones. Vos demás podí tomar un bus, porque trabajas en pleno centro, mientras que yo tengo que llevar el auto porque el micro no llega a esa parte de Bethesda.

Después de eso hice un esfuerzo por llegar siempre a tiempo aunque dos o tres veces me atrasé porque con una guagua es bien difícil. A veces se llena de pichí justo a la hora de partir o, qué sé yo, a veces devuelve la comida . . .

Un día no sólo llegué tarde sino que pa' más remate la guagua estaba bien resfriadita. Al principio ella no dijo nada pero miró a Bertito como si fuera un gusano y entonces miró a su niño y respiró. "Bueno," parece que estaba pensando, "¿qué se le puede hacer?" Esa noche me llamó y me dijo que Billy estaba empezando a toser y que por favor no fuera con Bertito al día siguiente.

—¿Y cómo se las va a arreglar usted? —le pregunté.

—Tendré que tomar el día no más —me dijo.

—Pero a usted le pagan igual, ¿no es cierto? —le pregunté.

—No —me dijo, bien cortante.

Después me explicó que su esposo se había puesto a rabiar como un demonio porque ella había tenido que quedarse en casa con el mocoso y me pidió que por favor, que no volviera a venir con la guagua resfriada.

—¿Y qué voy a hacer si un día Bertito amanece con catarro? —le pregunté.

—No sé —me dijo. —Cuestión suya. Tendría que encontrar con quién dejarlo.

Yo no sé si estaba realmente enfadada o si solamente estaba preocupada o tal vez cansada. Estaba parpadeando muy rápido y me pareció que estaba tratando de contener las lágrimas.

Después de eso todo anduvo bien por un tiempo. Claro que hubo uno que otro incidente. Una vez Bertito rompió el juguete favorito de Billy. Yo estaba bien asustada, y la señora Carolyn salió corriendo a reemplazarlo antes de que llegara su esposo y se diera cuenta.

—¿Para qué se lo vamos a mencionar a Charles? —me dijo sonriendo. —What he doesn't know won't hurt him.

Yo no entendí exactamente lo que quería decir con eso pero sí me di cuenta de que ella estaba tratando de protegerme y de protegerse a sí misma.

En diciembre la señora me llamó a la cocina y me dijo que pensaba darme cinco días de vacaciones: el 24, 25 y 26 de diciembre y entonces el Año Nuevo y el día anterior. Esos eran los días que le daban a ella en la oficina, me dijo. Yo estaba contenta y le di las gracias.

—Pídele toda la semana del 24 —me dijo Alberto. —A mí me dan toda la semana. Así podemos ir a Nueva York a visitar a mi hermano Fernando.

—No puedo —le dije. —Ella tiene que trabajar los otros días. A ella no le dan toda la semana libre.

—Pucha —dijo él. —¡Cómo dejái que esa gente se aproveche! Dile a la vieja que tení que tomar toda la semana no más. Si no le gusta que se vaya a la mierda.

—¿Y si me echa?

—Qué te va a echar. Te necesita. ¿Dónde más va a encontrar a alguien que se encargue del mocoso y le limpie la casa por treinta y cinco pesos al día?

—No sé —le dije. —No me gusta ponerle problemas. Se ha portado rebién conmigo.

Yo pensaba que la señora Carolyn se iba a enojar cuando le pedí el tiempo, pero me dijo que no me preocupara, que su esposo no trabajaba esa semana, la semana del 24, y a lo mejor él se podía encargar de Billy y de la Pámela, que también estaba de vacaciones del colegio. Se lo agradecí mucho.

Pero después, esa noche, me llamó por teléfono y me dijo que cuando le había propuesto a su marido que se ocupara de los niños para que yo pudiera ir a Nueva York a visitar a mi cuñado, él había puesto un grito en el cielo, que había dicho que era el colmo, que no solamente yo cobraba un dineral y llegaba con mi mocoso mugriento y enfermizo sino que ya me estaba dando aires de ejecutiva y pidiendo vacaciones pagadas y . . . qué sé yo . . . me dijo un montón de cosas más que yo no entendí.

Total, me fui con Alberto de todos modos, y cuando volví me fijé que la señora se había puesto algo seca conmigo . . . aunque ella sabía muy bien que yo no tenía la culpa.

Mientras tanto Alberto seguía fregando por lo de la plata.

—Treinta y siete al día aunque sean —me dijo.

—Es que me da pena —le dije.

—Es que nosotros necesitamos la plata.

—La tendríamos si vos tuvierai más cuidado —le dije. —¿Quién te dijo que salierai a comprar un estéreo? Pucha, si hace un año que no me compro un vestido.

—Esa es cosa aparte.

Esperé un par de días porque pensaba que la señora podía estar molesta todavía por la talla de las vacaciones. Entonces le pregunté cuándo podía esperar un aumento.

—Aunque sean un par de dólares al día —le dije. —Diez dólares más a la semana.

Ella dijo que encontraría la manera de conseguírmelos.

—Por favor, no se lo mencione a Charles —me dijo. —Los sacaré del dinero que me da para el mercado.

A mí no me importaba de adónde diablos los sacara. Lo único que quería yo era que Alberto dejara de molestar. Además, yo estaba trabajando muchas horas. Los malditos dos dólares al día me los merecía. Se suponía que yo me fuera a las cuatro, cuando ella llegaba del trabajo, pero por esa época mi hijito Berto estaba empezando a negarse a estar el día entero en la andadera. Ya caminaba y se metía en todo, no me dejaba hacer nada en la casa. Entonces muchas veces me quedaba hasta las cuatro y media o aún hasta las cinco para terminar de barrer o de sacudir . . . aunque no tenía la obligación de hacerlo . . . ¿me entiende? . . . porque el arreglo era que me fuera a las cuatro . . . pero me daba pena dejarla así con todo el aseo por hacer porque a veces venía agotada de la oficina. Tengo que reconocer que la señora Carolyn trabajaba bien duro, tan duro como yo.

Pero la talla es que se acostumbró a que me quedara hasta más tarde, y eso es lo que no me gustó. Empezó a llegar tarde siempre los martes, porque decía que estaba tomando una clase de ejercicios aeróbicos . . . baile y ejercicios combinados o no sé qué cosa . . . y que por favor me quedara hasta las cinco. Decía que le hacía falta hacer ejercicio porque tenía un trabajo muy sedentario, y eso es muy malo para la salud. "Le haría bien limpiar su propia casa si lo que necesita es hacer ejercicio," pensé.

Yo le dije que sí, que me quedaría, pero después me arrepentí porque a Alberto le cayó remal que yo llegara siempre tarde los martes. A Alberto le gusta que la comida esté en la mesa las ocho y si salgo a las cinco no llego a casa hasta las cinco y media o un cuarto para las seis. Y entre bañar a Bertito y darle de comer y hacer la cena . . . pues a veces me atraso y no alcanzo a tenerlo todo listo cuando llega Alberto.

—¿Y cómo que está tomando una clase? —me dijo.

—Sí —le dije. —La señora Carolyn insiste en que una mujer necesita eso. A lo mejor yo también debería tomar una clase de baile. ¿No veí como todas las americanas salen a trotar por la mañana? Se cuidan el cuerpo. No es como en los países de uno, donde la mujer de cuarenta años ya está vieja y gorda. La gringa es bien admirable.

—¿Y no dijistes que no tenían plata?

—¿Y?

—Pues, esas clases cuestan plata. ¿Qué? ¿Vos creí que es gratis?

Las cosas se echaron a perder definitivamente el día en que el señor no fue a trabajar. Estaba leyendo el periódico en el comedor cuando yo llegué.

—Goo mornee —le dije. Desgraciadamente nunca aprendí a pronunciar muy bien en inglés.

—Good morning —me dijo. Pero no me miró.

—¿Se encuentra usted mal hoy? —le pregunté. Me pareció bien raro que no fuera a trabajar. El no me contestó. Siguió mirando el diario y sorbiendo su café . . . si es que se le puede llamar café a esa agua sucia que toman los gringos . . .

Esa mañana me fue mal en todo. Bertito se había puesto increíblemente travieso. Apenas yo guardaba una cacerola, él la sacaba. Yo estaba tratando de distraerlo a él cuando Billy se acercó a la escalera. La verdad es que ni siquiera lo vi caerse, pero de repente oímos un grito y era que Billy se había tirado de cabeza por los peldaños. Bajé corriendo. Se había golpeado pero no pareció demasiado serio. Su papá lo examinó por todos lados. A mí me miró refeo, como si hubiera tenido la culpa yo. Le acarició la nuca y le dijo que no llorara, que se portara como un hombrecito. Dentro de poco el niño dejó de llorar. Le pregunté al señor si iba a llevarlo a la sala de emergencia para que lo chequearan. El dijo que no, que no le parecía necesario. El cabro ya estaba jugando en su cuarto, riéndose con un disco del Pato Donald. Fuera hijo mío, lo habría llevado a la clínica por si acaso.

—Rosa —me dijo el señor cuando la crisis había pasado —tengo que hacer un viaje de negocios la semana que viene. Voy a partir el lunes. Necesito que usted me lave y planche todas las camisas para que yo pueda hacer las maletas. ¿Me entiende, Rosa?"

A mí me carga que la gente me diga "¿Me entiende, Rosa?" como si fuera una idiota. Es cierto que no domino bien el inglés, pero no soy tonta, comprendo cuando me hablan. Bueno, él fue a su cuarto y se vistió y partió. Los dos niños no hicieron más que chillar ese día. Primero Berto le agarraba un juguete al otro y éste se ponía a gritar. Entonces Billy le daba una cachetada a Bertito o le tiraba el avioncito o le quitaba la frazadita. Estaba muy sublevado, a lo mejor por la caída. La verdad es que se me olvidaron las camisas.

Esa noche estábamos saliendo Alberto y yo cuando sonó el teléfono. Era la señora Carolyn.

—Charles está furioso —explicó. —Dijo que le pidió a usted que se ocupara de sus camisas y aquí están las camisas sin lavar.

—Ah —le dije. —No tuve tiempo.

—Bueno, Rosa —me respondió. —A usted le pagamos por hacer ciertas cosas y no podemos aceptar que no las haga.

—Mire, señora —le dije. —Pasaré mañana sábado en algún momento. ¿Está bien?

—Bueno —dijo. —No se olvide.

—¡Mierda! —dijo Alberto. —¡Vai a pasar el sábado planchando? ¿Y a mí me pensái dejar solo con el cabro?

—¿Qué se le puede hacer? Llevo al niño conmigo, si querí.

—Bueno —dijo, calmándose. —Por lo menos serán unos pesos extras. Cóbrale bien caro, ¿oístes? No es como si el sábado no fuera un día feriado.

El sábado estuvimos ocupadísimos Alberto y yo. Fuimos a Silver Spring a comprar una alfombra para el líving. ¿No ve que es el único día que tenemos para ocuparnos de nuestras cosas? También fuimos al mercado y llevamos la ropa sucia al laundromat porque no tenemos máquina en el departamento. Cenamos con un chico que trabaja con Alberto y con la polola de él . . . una niña relinda . . . uruguaya . . . Fuimos a un pequeño restaurante chileno que hay en el centro y comimos empanadas y pastel de choclo. Llegué donde la señora Carolyn como a las diez de la noche.

El abrió la puerta. Tenía cara de pocos amigos.

—Carolyn ya lavó las camisas —me dijo. —Sólo necesito que usted me las planche.

—Menos mal —le dije. Sólo tengo una hora. Mi marido regresa por mí a las once.

Bajé al basement y me puse a trabajar. Me había dejado doce camisas pero sólo logré planchar ocho.

—¿No va usted a terminar? —me preguntó la señora Carolyn.

—No puedo —le expliqué. —Alberto ya debe de estar esperándome en el auto delante de la casa.

Y entonces le dije: —Ah, señora Carolyn, usted me debe treinta y dos dólares.

—¿Y cómo?

—Por las camisas. Alberto me dijo que le cobrara cuatro pesos por camisa.

La señora Carolyn se puso lívida.

—¿Y usted piensa que le voy a pagar extra por hacer lo que debería haber hecho ayer? ¿Cómo se le ocurre? Mire, Rosa —me dijo. Apenas podía articular las palabras. Era como si se le atragantaran. —Nosotros hemos sido bien flexibles con usted. Dejamos que venga con su niño, y no crea que yo no sé que usted se pasa el día entero tonteando con él en vez de limpiar la casa.

—Yo pongo un día bien largo, señora —le dije.

Allí es donde perdió la calma. Empezó a enredarse con el español . . . a decir dos palabras en inglés y una en castellano.

—¡Un día bien largo! —balbuceó.

Y entonces se descolgó con una gorda. —Pedazo de mierda —gritó. —Pedazo de mierda (o algo por el estilo, sólo reconocí la palabra "shit" y algunas otras barbaridades). ¿Tú pones un día bien largo? Tú trabajas unas dos horas al día en esta casa. El resto del tiempo estás cambiándole los pañales sucios a tu mocoso. Nosotros le pagamos exactamente lo que le pagaríamos a una mujer americana que hablara inglés y que pudiera llamar al doctor en una emergencia, que no estuviera aquí de ilegal, que pusiera ocho horas de trabajo . . . y tú te portas como una mierda con nosotros. ¡Porquería!

—Algo así me dijo.

Entonces se echó a llorar.

Don Charles se metió la mano al bolsillo y sacó treinta y dos dólares.

La señora Carolyn seguía: —Y tú piensas que te vamos a pagar un día entero por una hora de trabajo que hiciste. Si hemos estado esperándote todo el día. Ni siquiera llamaste. No sabíamos si venías o si no venías. Y de repente apareces a las diez de la noche y haces un par de cosas y exiges que te paguemos casi un día entero. Por Dios, Rosa, por Dios.

Hipaba mientras hablaba. Ya no estaba gritando.

—Cálmate —le dijo él. —No te aflijas, Carolyn. Total, ¿qué se le puede esperar a una mujer así? Por una mujer así no vale la pena afligirse.

—Tome —dijo, tendiéndome el dinero. —Y no vuelva.

—No se preocupe —le dije. —No pienso volver.

A mí también se me llenaban los ojos de lágrimas.

Al subir al auto le conté a Alberto lo que había pasado.

—No importa —me dijo. —Encontrarás otro trabajo.

Pero me di cuenta de que no estaba nada contento porque la que realmente mantiene a la familia soy yo. El no gana casi nada allí donde trabaja.

—No sé por qué esto tuvo que pasar —le dije.

—Cosa de mujeres —contestó Alberto. —No pueden estar sin armar boches . . . siempre peleando . . .

—Y justo ahora —dije. —Justo cuando el señor se va de viaje. ¿Qué va a hacer la señora Carolyn? No puede faltar al trabajo . . .

—Que se las arregle como pueda.

Pero la verdad es que me da pena esa mujer. Muchas veces pienso en ella y me pregunto cómo le ha ido, si encontró a otra muchacha o si deja a Billy en una guardería . . . pobre niño . . . era un amor de chicoco . . . y ella . . . era redije, resimpática. Me gustaba trabajar en su casa. A veces tengo ganas de llamarla para ver cómo está . . . pero sé que no se puede. Es una lástima. De veras. Es una lástima.

The Scholarship Jacket

Marta Salinas

The small Texas school that I went to had a tradition carried out every year during the eighth grade graduation: a beautiful gold and green jacket (the school colors) was awarded to the class valedictorian, the student who had maintained the highest grades for eight years. The scholarship jacket had a big gold S on the left front side and your name written in gold letters on the pocket.

My oldest sister Rosie had won the jacket a few years back and I fully expected to also. I was fourteen and in the eighth grade. I had been a straight A student since the first grade and this last year had looked forward very much to owning that jacket. My father was a farm laborer who couldn't earn enough money to feed eight children, so when I was six I was given to my grandparents to raise. We couldn't participate in sports at school because there were registration fees, uniform costs, and trips out of town; so, even though our famly was quite agile and athletic there would never be a school sports jacket for us. This one, the scholarship jacket, was our only chance.

In May, close to graduation, spring fever had struck as usual with a vengeance. No one paid any attention in class; instead we stared out the windows and at each other wanting to speed up the last few weeks of school. I despaired every time I looked in the mirror. Pencil thin, not a curve anywhere, I was called "beanpole" and "string bean" and I knew that's what I looked like. A flat chest, no hips, and a brain, that's what I had. That really wasn't much for a fourteen-year-old to work with, I thought, as I absentmindedly wandered from my history class to the gym. Another hour of sweating in basketball and displaying my toothpick legs was coming up. Then I remembered my P.E. shorts were still in a bag under my desk where I'd forgotten them. I had to wallk all the way back and get them. Coach Thompson was a real bear if someone wasn't dressed for P.E. She had said I was a good forward and even tried to talk Grandma into letting me join the team once. Of course Grandma said no.

I was almost back at my classroom door when I heard voices raised in anger as if in some sort of argument. I stopped. I didn't mean to eavesdrop, I just hesitated, not knowing what to do. I needed those shorts and I was going to be late, but I didn't want to interrupt an argument between my teachers. I recognized the voices: Mr. Schmidt, my history teacher, and Mr. Boone, my math teacher. They seemed to be arguing about me. I couldn't believe it. I still remember the feeling of shock that rooted me flat against the wall as if I were trying to blend in with the graffiti written there.

"I refuse to do it! I don't care who her father is, her grades don't even begin to compare to Martha's. I won't lie or falsify records. Martha has a straight A-plus average and you know it." That was Mr. Schmidt and he sounded very angry. Mr. Boone's voice sounded calm and quiet.

"Look, Joann's father is not only on the Board, he owns the only store in town; we could say it was a close tie and—"

The pounding in my ears drowned out the rest of the words, only a word here and there filtered through. ". . . Martha is Mexican . . . resign . . . won't do it. . . ." Mr. Schmidt came rushing out and luckily for me went down the opposite way toward the auditorium, so he didn't see me. Shaking, I waited a few minutes and then went in and grabbed my bag and fled from the room. Mr. Boone looked up when I came in but didn't say anything. To this day I don't remember if I got in trouble in P.E. for being late or how I made it through the rest of the afternoon. I went home very sad and cried into my pillow that night so Grandmother wouldn't hear me. It seemed a cruel coincidence that I had overheard that conversation.

The next day when the principal called me into his office I knew what it would be about. He looked uncomfortable and unhappy. I decided I wasn't going to make it any easier for him so I looked him straight in the eyes. He looked away and fidgeted with the papers on his desk.

"Martha," he said, "there's been a change in policy this year regarding the scholarship jacket. As you know, it has always been free." He cleared his throat and continued. "This year the Board has decided to charge fifteen dollars, which still won't cover the complete cost of the jacket."

I stared at him in shock and a small sound of dismay escaped my throat. I hadn't expected this. He still avoided looking in my eyes.

"So if you are unable to pay the fifteen dollars for the jacket it will be given to the next one in line." I didn't need to ask who that was.

Standing with all the dignity I could muster, I said, "I'll speak to my grandfather about it, sir, and let you know tomorrow." I cried on the walk home from the bus stop. The dirt road was a quarter mile from the highway, so by the time I got home, my eyes were red and puffy.

"Where's Grandpa?" I asked Grandma, looking down at the floor so she wouldn't ask me why I'd been crying. She was sewing on a quilt as usual and didn't look up.

"I think he's out back working in the bean field."

I went outside and looked out at the fields. There he was. I could see him walking between the rows, his body bent over the little plants, hoe in and. I walked slowly out to him, trying to think how I could best ask him for the money. There was a cool breeze blowing and a sweet smell of mesquite fruit in the air but I didn't appreciate it. I kicked at a dirt clod. I wanted that jacket so much. It was more than just being a valedictorian and giving a little thank you speech for the jacket on graduation night. It represented eight years of hard work and expectation. I knew I had to be honest with Grandpa; it was my only chance. He saw my shadow and looked up.

He waited for me to speak. I cleared my throat nervously and clasped my hands behind my back so he wouldn't see them shaking. "Grandpa, I have a big favor to ask you," I said in Spanish, the only language he knew. He still waited silently. I tried again. "Grandpa, this year the principal said the scholarship jacket is not going to be free. It's going to cost fifteen dollars, and I have to take the money in tomorrow, otherwise it'll be given to someone else." The last words came out in an eager rush. Grandpa straightened up tiredly and leaned his chin on the hoe handle. He looked out over the field that was filled with the tiny green bean plants. I waited, desperately hoping he'd say I could have the money.

He turned to me and asked quietly, "What does a scholarship jacket mean?"

I answered quickly; maybe there was a chance. "It means you've earned it by having the highest grades for eight years and that's why they're giving it to you." Too late I realized the significance of my words. Grandpa knew that I understood it was not a matter of money. It wasn't that. He went back to hoeing the weeds that sprang up between the delicate little bean plants. It was a time-consuming job; sometimes the small shoots were right next to each other. Finally he spoke again as I turned to leave, crying.

"Then if you pay for it, Marta, it's not a scholarship jacket, is it? Tell your principal I will not pay the fifteen dollars."

I walked back to the house and locked myself in the bathroom for a long time. I was angry with Grandfater even though I knew he was right, and I was angry with the Board, whoever they were. Why did they have to change the rules just when it was my turn to win the jacket? Those were the days of belief and innocence.

It was a very sad and withdrawn girl who dragged into the principal's office the next day. This time he did look me in the eyes.

"What did your grandfather say?"

I sat very straight in my chair.

"He said to tell you he won't pay the fifteen dollars."

The principal muttered something I couldn't understand under his breath and walked over to the window. He stood looking out at something outside. He looked bigger than usual when he stood up; he was a tall, gaunt man with gray hair, and I watched the back of his head while I waited for him to speak.

"Why?" he finally asked. "Your grandfather has the money. He owns a two-hundred acre ranch."

I looked at him, forcing my eyes to stay dry. "I know, sir, but he said if I had to pay for it, then it wouldn't be a scholarship jacket." I stood up to leave. "I guess you'll just have to give it to Joann." I hadn't meant to say that, it had just slipped out. I was almost to the door when he stopped me.

"Martha—wait."

I turned and looked at him, waiting. What did he want now? I could feel my heart pounding loudly in my chest and see my blouse fluttering where my breasts should have been. Something bitter and vile tasting was coming up in my mouth; I was afraid I was going to be sick. I didn't need any sympathy speeches. He sighed loudly and went back to his big desk. He watched me, biting his lip.

"Okay, damn it. We'll make an exception in your case. I'll tell the Board, you'll get your jacket."

I could hardly believe my ears. I spoke in a trembling rush. "Oh, thank you, sir!" Suddenly I felt great. I didn't know about adrenalin in those days, but I knew something was pumping through me, making me feel as tall as the sky. I wanted to yell, jump, run the mile, do something. I ran out so I could cry in the hall where there was no one to see me.

At the end of the day, Mr. Schmidt winked at me and said, "I hear you're getting the scholarship jacket this year."

His face looked as happy and innocent as a baby's, but I knew better. Without answering I gave him a quick hug and ran to the bus. I cried on the walk home again, but this time because I was so happy. I couldn't wait to tell Grandpa and ran straight to the field. I joined him in the row where he was working and without saying anything I crouched down and started pulling up the weeds with my hands. Grandpa worked alongside me for a few minutes and he didn't ask what had happened. After I had a little pile of weeds between the rows, I stood up and faced him.

"The principal said he's making an exception for me, Grandpa, and I'm getting the jacket after all. That's after I told him what you said."

Grandpa didn't say anything, he just gave me a pat on the shoulder and a smile. He pulled out the crumpled red handkerchief that he always carried in his back pocket and wiped the sweat off his forehead.

"Better go see if your grandmother needs any help with supper."

I gave him a big grin. He didn't fool me. I skipped and ran back to the house whistling some silly tune.

VI. GALANES

Antihero

Ana Castillo

I don't know why a man is sometimes attracted to the insolence of a certain woman. It is true that I am a passionate man. I even thrive on the obstacles to winning her, while at the same time I grow to detest her immensely for all that I must endure!

She called me, for instance, at the last moment, to join her in attending a film. It was rare that she should call, I admit, and that made me instantly susceptible to her game. Elsewise, I might have gone on with my evening and not given her call any significance. But I agreed to meet her at a quarter to the hour.

It began to rain as I waited in front of the theater, and for ten minutes I searched the black street with my eyes for some sign that she was indeed coming.

I thought about our brief telephone conversation. We'd talked about our work. We did not mention Laura, who was out of town anyway. Why couldn't she be like Laura? Laura, like the vulnerable spring, open and ready to give and to be given, never had me waiting in the rain. But it was exactly that she was nothing like Laura that attracted me to her.

When she did appear, not five minutes too soon, she mumbled about not having been able to find a parking space, avoiding any apology as always. Immediately I sensed her intensity, her power of destruction, and repented having come — not because I feared she could destroy me, do some irreversible harm to my life, ruin the safe assurance of my relationship with Laura, but because it is frustrating to be so aware that such a woman exists!

I hesitated to invite her for a drink afterward, thinking I'd do better returning home and catching up on my work or getting a good night's rest. She drinks as well as any man, and I knew one drink would lead to another and before the night ended for us we would be exchanging insults on the street, in the rain, without consideration of the hour or the peaceful souls sleeping in surrounding buildings.

Once I thought I felt enough vengeance to kill her, put my hands tightly around her bird-like neck and crush the delicate bones within. I swore that night it would be well worth it if I had to spend the rest of my days in prison. But of course I didn't do it.

Instead I married Laura. It was a practical step in every sense of the word. The authorities were threatening to have me thrown out of the country, and with Laura's political pull, or rather that of her father, I was freed through our marriage. For a time, perhaps months or only weeks, I felt a surge of tranquility and my insatiable restlessness subsided.

Once, when Laura was away, I called *her,* that cancerous sore of my existence. To my surprise, she was receptive and invited me to see her that same evening. We twisted like live wires in an explosion of passion, so that days, weeks later, I bathed in the aftermath of our interlude.

Like the greedy bastard that I am, it was a given that I'd have to see her again. The only excruciating detail of all this clandestine maneuvering was not making certain Laura would not find out but not letting *her* know what it all meant to me — to see her, be with her, alone again.

I went ahead and asked her to have the drink with me. To my surprise, and sudden rage, she declined. She said nothing of having another appointment, but the mere thought of it made me insist. I found myself tugging at her arm like some common beggar, while she looked around apparently concerned about those who noticed my sense of urgency as they passed. She examined her fingernails, as she sometimes does when I know she is conceiving some miserable plan for me; her small hands like wings fluttered before my blurred vision.

Without a word she complied, walking across the street to the bar that gives a complimentary drink to all patrons of the theater. As soon as we sat down and I went to the bar to get the two dry red wines, she lit a cigarette. I loathe cigarette smoke, particularly hers. Immediately I regretted being so irrationally persistent. I should have let her go on her way. With any luck, she might have been accosted and I'd have read about her in the papers the next morning.

Her extraordinary silence masks her as a patient listener, complimenting my weakness for airing my views. I rambled on about my latest work while she nodded occasionally, interjecting a question. As expected, one drink led to the next, and it seemed no time had passed when the lights went on to signal that the establishment was about to close.

When we got on our coats and stumbled out into the wet night, I saw that the moon was almost full, very white, and I shuddered. "Only when I see you does the moon appear that way," I slurred absurdly. She almost laughed, a low huff from the throat. She can be so devastatingly cynical I'd like to cast her in iron, make a monument to society: Ode to the State of Affairs.

She reached effortlessly into her small pocketbook for her keys. The hint of gold on her finger flashed before me. "What is this?" I said, at first attempting to keep my façade of indifference. I held up her left hand on which the band was placed on the tale-telling finger. Many nights of drunken carousing with colleagues, when we set out to conquer all, began with my noticing if the victim was already spoken for, so to speak. Of course it had never mattered, but *her* . . .?

She pulled her hand away, hid it deep in her pocket. She laughed again, not from the chest, but from the throat. It was nerve wracking. "But . . . why . . . with whom?" I heard myself blurting. I was following her to her car, not walking together, not arm in arm as we sometimes did, but behind, fast on her heels. We were stepping quickly and it was beginning to rain again.

"Why didn't you tell me?" I asked the same question another way. She refused to look at me. Suddenly she stopped, with that old mocking expression she reserves for knowing that I am shedding the armor, relinquishing the farce. "What do you care, Max? What the hell do you care?"

I stood there, watching her dark figure disappear like a shadow, speechless. I'd have to think about that, I thought, and turned back to look for a bar that wouldn't close before I could lose all my senses.

House Calls on 15th Street

Andrea-Teresa Arenas

Leaving the crowded bar,
cruising home
he pivots midstream   to continue his search

Waking her from restless sleep
he rings her doorbell,
gaunt,
tired, with lipgloss smudges on his collar,
he asks to share her bed.

Too afraid to say no
she opens her door to this man of multiplicities.

His satin tie drops to the floor
and with it falls his bravado.
Shirt thrown across the dresser
and with it lies his arrogance.
Slacks and underwear lie at the foot of her bed
and with them rests his machismo.

Briefly scanning his nakedness in the mirror
he begins to rattle off the day's events.
Broken glass disclosures
sputter from his brown velvet lips.

After sweaty adventures under the weight of comforters
he folds into a fetal cocoon
and asks to be held.

Dozing off to dreamless sleep
neither one admits
lonely people do not make love,
they   only wrestle with the shadows of sex.

Curve Ball

Andrea-Teresa Arenas

This vato primes,
            turns tricks,
            delivers slick orations
all
            for La Raza.

This vato struts,
            sways,
            juggles the books,
            and the lives of people,
all
            para La Raza.

He slips her between
rumpled sheets
to mount her missionary style

todo
            para La Raza.

Gracias, querido mío

Marjorie Agosín

Gracias por dejarme humedecida
y no de emoción
con tu toalla estrangulada
al toilet
gracias por haberme enredado en el olor
de tus calcetines
recostados sobre la dura tez de tus zapatos,
gracias querido mío por haberme despertado
y comunicado de tu dolor de muelas
tu dolor de dedos
las úlceras que se te avecinan.

Gracias por haberme declarado tu
compañera
y conducirme apegada entre tus piernas
a reuniones de señores elegantes
donde tu pobre niña se margina en las esquinas
mientras tú me pides un escarbadientes.

Gracias por declararme tan mundana
al pedirme que escriba tus cartas
porque mal que mal a mí también me equivocaron
de profesión
y para dactilógrafa me amaestraron.

Gracias querido mío
por roncar en mi esplada
cuando no deseo precisamente tus ronquidos
ni tus pies duros
ni tus deseos de llevarme a la luna,
con un viaje a la playa
me conformaría.

En fin
gracias por hacerme entender
que mi lugar
no está junto
al tuyo.

León

(Para Leonidas)

Marjorie Agosín

Comprendo que era imposible
que te enamoraras de mí
porque no me seduce la
idea de la conquista.
Dejémoslo para Hernán Cortés y sus compadres.
Además,
nunca sé cómo colocar las piernas,
en qué ranura juntarlas,
ni cómo tomar el delgadísimo cigarrillo,
enjaulado en los dedos del deseo.

No sé de discreciones
y el silencio sólo fue
el instrumento de las
hermanas monjas
de las hermanas suicidas
de las ahogadas porque sí en el lago del olvido.

En cambio yo,
lanzo el canto de la locura,
osada me desnudo ante los intrusos
maravillados por mi cuerpo al aire
y fajado de tules incandescentes
hablo, pienso, y me río a carcajadas.

Me seduce ser tan simplemente yo,
colmar los espacios de inverosímiles preguntas,
comer con la boca abierta,
masticar profundamente una cebolla
porque así olemos nosotras, las mujeres,
las enemigas del pudoroso sudor de la mantequilla,
somos iconoclastas,
parricidas.

Para alguien que no sabe cantar

Eliana Rivero

ni siquiera silbando se recuerda
la última noche que no pasé contigo;
ni en francés
ni en nahuatl
ni en ninguna otra lengua inventariada
se podría contar
ese episodio misterioso de adoquines
en un barrio del norte,
de gasas entreabiertas a la luz
en la mañana que no queríamos tocar

todo un aire se alzaba desde el río
con ojos y señales,
y lo dejamos
que se muriera con los gallos;
lo matamos con ideas corteses
en una madrugada de zodíacos,
lo asesinamos en una posterior locura
de almejas y borrachos,
de crustáceos y de escaleras empinadas
que no llegaron a ninguna parte
porque se entretuvieron
con la letra de canciones antiguas
que nos hacían añorar
las idas al colegio en la tarde
de mil novecientos cincuenta
y aquellos tiempos en que no sabíamos
que ni siquiera silbando se recuerda
algo que nunca sucedió

The Ripening

Alma Villanueva

The snow began to blind her, making her senses more acute. Already it was February, Ground Hog Day had come and gone, and the snowflakes only seemed to grow larger, more beautiful, floating with supreme confidence to the earth. Lucía alternated between watching snow drifts deepen with childlike wonder and maternal dread. After all, she was in charge of this show, this small family. But her senses, her senses (and she didn't fully realize this) were absolutely wide open. The wind was harsh, gentle, filled with messages. Truly the snow fell on her body; the cushioned silence of the snow seemed to allow each cell to blossom it its blood.

Yet this had come after a great dispersion, when she'd given her body away, piece by piece, limb by limb, to her husband. Once she read about the ancient practice of shamans, who fall into a trance and then meet an adversary, a power that would render them into pieces. After this painful scattering of their body, it was their task, a very difficult one—in fact, it wasn't always completed—to reassemble themselves: to re-member themselves, whole. This is how she felt (though she didn't know this yet, at this time in February): gathered, intensely whole, and every blossom open, each startling fragrance separate, and at once harmonious.

Here, in the snow, in her cabin, Lucía built a fire, daily, in winter. Alone but for her child, some friends, some neighbors out of eye-distance. Here, she fed her fire, log by log, and without design or a conscious knowing reassembled herself. That other fire had not required cedar, pine or oak, but her very willing body—a breast, the other breast, the lips, the entire spine. Yes, as the shamans had to meet the feared entity to become it, its desirable qualities, she went to meet the masculine in the form of her husband, in the utterly pleasurable, utterly painful realm of romantic love: that trance.

Lucía learned to be on the alert, a strange middle ground of expecting without expecting, when disasters occurred. This, she learned at last, was the time, the timing when the switch into its opposite was most ripe. Though, like anyone else, she muttered, "shit, fuck, damn it," then reminded herself to watch for anything.

She's standing at the sink doing her dishes when something makes her turn and look out the kitchen window. Huge billows of steam are rising in the eight degree air—"Jesus S. Christ," she mutters and runs outside. Hot water spurts out from under the house—cracked water pipe, she thinks. Runs in, turns off the hot water heater, grabs the child, puts him in the baby seat, and goes for help.

The regular neighbor she counts on for a slashed tire once, a burning electric wire another time, isn't home; a car with a man and a woman begins to pull out of a half-finished cabin. Here in the mountains everyone is a possibility in an emergency, so: "Do you know anything about plumbing?" "Yeah," answers the young, reddish-blonde man.

I remember him, thinks Lucía. He's that guy who had his car parked in the middle of the road and then made a big deal about me backing up my car, as if I'd been in the way. Just walked right up to my car, not a muscle moving in his face, his eyes connecting directly to mine, and with his lips hardly moving said, "Would you move your car back, so I can get around you?" Boy-hypnotist, she thought. Lucía paused, almost giggled, but strangely intrigued said, "Sure." She backed up, staying on the road, making him go around her, angrily, in a cloud of dust. Boy-wonder, Lucía murmured. Actually he wasn't a boy, but a man in his twenties — still, something reminded her of her older son.

She led the way to her house, feeling the woman beside him arch her eyebrows. "There it is. I guess the hot water's almost gone. I turned off the water heater," Lucía informs him. He tries to pretend he doesn't hear her but proceeds to discover the leak on his own, stepping around in the mud. "Broken water pipe," he says to the house.

"Pardon *me*?" Lucía asks.

"Broken hot water pipe," he grudgingly responds. "How do you get down there?"

"Where?" Lucía torments him just slightly, her eyes suggesting his feet standing in the mud.

"Under the house," he tells the house again.

"Why don't we look inside. The only place I can think of is my closets," Lucía responds soberly.

The woman, standing on some large rocks to avoid the mud, feels the tension and goes to the car, probably slightly embarrassed because he treats women so nastily. Lucía had seen her mouth fall open a couple of times — most likely Lucía's strength brought out the worst in him and also something he couldn't quite put his finger on. Lucía could see that if one did the preliminary surrender, he'd be tolerable — but no, he would have to tolerate her as well. Lucía didn't like how the woman held herself, soft-stomached, unprotected, the weary look in her eyes, and not even a trace of lipstick. Lucía liked lipstick, it gave her a vivid look, she thought. I may be dying, a raging fever, and incurable illness, maybe just old enough to kiss it goodbye — let me apply a fresh one first.

Lucía begins to lead the way to the house, holding her youngest, and he walks right past her into the house without the slightest effort to wipe his boots, though she senses his effort not to. Barbarian — she stares at his feet and tolerates the footprints by holding her breath and the word "barbarian." She imagines the vacuum cleaner running after he's gone.

He searches both closet floors and surmises he'll have to cut through one to get to the pipe. He walks to the front door and says to her desk: "I'll turn off your water till tomorrow. I'll be here first thing in the morning. See ya."

"What's your name?"

He stops as though collared, turns, and flashes his eyes right into hers. "Jess. What's yours?"

"Lucía," to his reddish-blonde hairline.

"Okay Lucy, see ya then."

"Lucía," she repeats evenly, right between his eyes.

"Right," he takes personal offense. With a name like that, no wonder, he smirks; uppity.

After Jess leaves, Lucía feels a familiar anger course through her body — broken hot water pipe. How apt, she thinks. So much heat inside, so much damn heat, and this cold, cold weather surrounding me. She laughs to herself, at herself. Well, at least he'll fix the damned pipe.

As she starts a late afternoon fire, she softens slightly toward Jess — he's afraid of me, like a little boy, or rather a big boy around sixteen or seventeen who hasn't come to terms with Mama. Handsome, well-built as far as I can see, but those glinting little eyes, and that mean, straight mouth (nicely shaped though — if his lips would relax she would see his hunger, Lucía well knew).

Little boys, little boys, in such big, strong bodies — Jesus, he makes me sick! Having lit the fire she was comforted, and she added a fine piece of pine.

Very early in the morning a banging at the door jolts her. Oh god, it's The Barbarian, she thinks as he enters without glancing at her, walking straight to the bedroom closet.

"Good morning," she says loudly.

"Yeah, hi." Straight to the closet, tool box down, on his knees, neck bent forward — rows and rows of thick reddish hair curl up beyond his teeshirt — with a neck like a baby bull.

"Call out if you need anything," Lucía states before firmly closing the hall door so the baby will say out.

I'll be damned if I'll ask him if he wants coffee. I hope he can smell it and is driven to ask for a cup, which I'll pour for him. How silly. The hell I will. I'll point to the stove, to the little white pot of his desire. And I'll let him know he can take it or leave it; it, of course, means nothing to me. If he drank coffee, he'd be human. Right, she reasons.

"I found it," he yells.

Lucía runs into the bedroom, "What?" (Gold, god, the eternal secret?)

"The trap door," he says to Lucía in his excitement. "It was under these rugs. I'll cover it up real good so no cold air leaks in later."

Concern, Lucía thinks, concern? "Thanks."

He flushes, red, up to his neck.

"Do you want some coffee?"

"Nah, the sooner I get this job done the better. I charge by the hour, you know."

Lucía leaves again, blocking him out entirely as she closes the hall door.

An hour passes. She goes into the closet and yells down the trap door, "You still alive?"

He laughs, "Yeah, I guess so."

He laughs, she notes. "How's it going?"

"Got the pipe, I'm insulating it. There's another part I have to get when I go into town."

Another fucking hour, Lucía says inwardly.

Jess appears at the trap door, the earth so soft she doesn't hear him, his eyes looking up at her with sneaky satisfaction. Startled, she laughs, "You look disembodied!"

"Thanks." Jess climbs up and stands directly opposite her for the first time, and for the first time the magnetism between them plays against her body, then his, to their mutual discomfort. They both shift simultaneously, noting this phenomenom with an "Oh no" and "Well, that's interesting."

"Listen, I'm going to town anyway, so I'll pick up the part. No sweat," he says to the bedroom door.

"Okay," she says to the rug.

"You ought to prune all the dead stuff off that aloe vera plant." (A huge plant she'd taken outside in summer for direct sunlight, which both dogs pissed on, causing some of the outer leaves to darken, but the central ones are new and green.)

"It would shock it to death," Lucía says defensively.

"Suit yourself," Jess smiles; his lips soften, expand.

He is the epitome of what I cannot stand. I don't believe it. You do what I say, body, Lucía commands herself, as he slams the door unnecessarily hard.

The Barbarian returns the next morning, not as early, with a slightly softer knock, and a "Hi" uttered carefully, from the back of his throat, slipping through his sharp, neat teeth like a small, smooth pebble.

"What's happening?" Lucía dumps a boulder in his path.

Jess slightly stumbles, composes his shoulders, and marches right through it with, "Not much."

Suit yourself, baby bull. I'm not even wearing red today, just purple, Lucía calmly relects. But the house is alive with a crackling red energy. She makes more coffee, hauls in wood, notices how soft the air is becoming, how good the earth smells, the spring beginning to prepare itself in her very womb. A new womb is exactly what I need, she smiles inside. Outside, her face looks puzzled, attentive, serious. The weather's warming, and so am I, Lucía feels.

As she returns to her kitchen she is startled to see Jess sitting with his legs spread apart, with the baby poking at him, coffee to his side. He is actually smiling as he asks the baby, "Do you fox trot yet, buddy?" Jess sees Lucía and doesn't stiffen at all and says, "He's all right. Pretty chunky. Strong little guy, aren't you?" letting him hang between his knees.

This is too much, Lucía muses, too much. "Did you eat breakfast?"

"Nah."

"Do you want some eggs?"

"Sure." (With a bit of enthusiasm.)

"Do you like hot stuff?"

"Sure." (Amused)

She makes huevos rancheros. He takes his to the couch. She sits on a stool dividing the kitchen and front room. The baby climbs on the couch trying to get to his food. "Bad spot," Lucía warns him. Jess just keeps eating and tolerating the attacks on his food.

"How much do I owe you?"

"Thirty bucks."

Lucía is astounded—she was sure it'd be fifty. "Really?"

"Yeah, it didn't take much."

"Great," Lucía smiles in spite of herself. "And thanks for coming two days in a row."

Without a word Jess gets up and takes his plate to the sink, washes it, grabs the pan and washes it too.

"Thanks," Lucía says and means it.

"I love Mexican food," he looks at her evenly.

His eyes are pretty intense, even if they are blue, she realizes as she looks away. "Have you ever gone to Mexico?"

"I went about twice a year for a few years, to the different festivals. The people there are pretty laid back—everybody dancing with everybody. I got pretty wasted on tequila the last time—woke up two days later."

"How old are you?"

"Twenty-six."

"My oldest son is twenty."

Jess looks astounded and smiles as though a secret had just been revealed to him.

"Who was that woman with you the other day?" Lucía asks.

"An old girlfriend. We see each other sometimes. She lives in the valley. A real neat lady."

They scan each other, eye to eye—the air between them quite still. The Barbarian is on leave, Lucía remembers.

"Are you going to be home tonight?"

"Probably."

"Do you mind if I come by?"

"Sounds fine."

"Do you drink wine?"

"I sure do."

"What kind? White or red?"

"How about white?"

"See you around seven?"

"Sure."

Jess begins to walk away, forgetting his tool belt. "Hey, your tools." Lucía picks them up and hands them to him. Jess stretches out his hands to receive them and they're trembling.

"Thanks," he says without raising his eyes and leaves Lucía trembling.

She bathes the baby, does some typing, takes a walk—her body feels hollow but good, like a flute. The way the wind prefers, she thinks.

When Jess arrives, the baby is asleep to Lucía's surprise. The bath, of course. How convenient, she reflects, and how scary—there's no distraction. My god, he's dressed up—a nice shirt, clean jeans; even cologne? Jess comes in and throws his down vest on a chair revealing very nice shoulders, his shirt tucked into slim hips—that neck is delicious, Lucía inhales and exhales softly. He hands her an album, Brazilian music (I don't believe it), Almaden Chablis (I don't believe this either, she thinks).

Then, they are awkward with each other; it is evident that they want to make love immediately, on the floor, the couch—immediately. So, Lucía puts on the record, he opens the wine, finds the glasses, pours. She gets cheese, some fruit—it's worse. She walks outside to get more wood. The cold air jabs her, closes her pores. The night is sobering in its darkness, its cool, light stars. So distant, she thinks, that's why they're cool. Actually, they're burning up—each glittering star up there. She returns into the house with an altered perspective and sits next to him on the couch after adding an oak log, perfectly.

"You build a good fire."

"I've built a fire nearly every day this winter. I love fires, they keep me company."

"I know what you mean."

As they talk about families, friends, the children they were, she catches him looking at her sideways, longways, piercingly. This is no ordinary young guy, and she realizes she's probably looking at him in the same way.

"Why don't you sell your house and come to Brazil with me? I could work on houses, there's a lot of building for the middle class, so I hear. We could buy a boat." The Brazilian music is playing. Yes, she loves Brazilian music. She could dance herself into a frenzy every time.

"I'm afraid I can't do that now, and besides I'd have to be the captain," Lucía laughs. "Do you know about the shit going on in El Salvador and Guatemala? Those are poor, poor places, Jess. It tears my heart out to just think of it. I personally wouldn't want to be part of any of that, if you know what I mean."

"Yeah, it's heavy." he says, adding a pine piece pretty much on center. He pauses and adds another one, and the fire blazes.

"I see you don't fool around."

"No way."

"Look, Jess, I'm really tired. Do you want to sleep on the couch since it's almost three?"

"Sounds good."

Lucía brings a sheet, some blankets. "Good night."

"Good night," Jess says, gently.

Lucía leaves him sitting there watching his fire, cursing herself and shivering as she enters the cool bed. My goddamn body's on fire, she moans to herself as she rushes to sleep.

The next morning the baby wakes her up early, as usual. She tiptoes by Jess, still asleep on the couch, with thick, curly red hair sticking out of the covers—he looks so vulnerable she could squeeze in beside him to feel his warmth, to see that his dreams smell like. Still like a little boy, I bet, Lucía guesses, like damp forests and the insides of shiny, new cars. I've never been attracted to anyone so young and so blunt (and so secretly promising and innocent), like a son, she sighs.

Lucía puts on the water for coffee, warms the bottle, opens the curtains, and sits to stare out the window in a dreamy fashion. This is when thinking is best, she thinks, fresh out of dreams. The deep fuchsia, wild roses begin to bud after that last deep snow she thought would never disappear. When they finally open, wide and beckoning, she imagines herself bending to smell each little womb. If our wombs were flowers, that's what their fragrance would be. For such small flowers, they were surprisingly intoxicating. They make her own womb, nipples, clitoris, swell and stir. She loved to smell them. She'd love to smell Jess right now, almost in the same way.

This all reminded her of something she put at the bottom of herself, guarded, so secretive it just filtered up, blindly, in the image of her older son. That last year with her. The quarrels, the conflict, the tension, and the love so tangible both could barely let go. He was taller than her, and a beard shadowed his face; his eyes were steady and questioning, his body as graceful as a boy's and as compelling as a man's. Yes, the thought had flickered like a tongue of a very ancient fire, and in that instant she gave him to another woman.

"Are you making coffee, Lucy?" Jess asks, throaty and warm, with mischief.

"Yes, I am, Cave Boy."

He laughs, "I'm gettin up," and walks to the bathroom relaxed and with a certain grace. With grace, she thinks. Not that heavy, hoofy foot that proclaims a MAN is in the house. Spare me. Where did The Barbarian go, she wonders.

Lucía gives the baby his bottle and returns to fix eggs and chorizo, tortillas.

"Far out, I love choreesso," Jess murmurs.

"That's what you get. How'd you sleep?" she asks, cool, cooler than she feels.

"Great," he looks at her without flinching. (Touché, his eyes whisper.) "This is delicious. Thanks. Got some more coffee?"

Lucía begins to reach for it, and Jess jumps up and motions toward her if she wants any. She nods yes, and he pours into both cups.

"Well, I'd better get down to the job. We'll be finishing up the house in a couple of weeks." He grabs the pot off the stove and washes it in scalding water and soap, putting it to dry on the stove in one movement.

"My contribution, Lucy."

"Thanks, Cave Boy."

They stand and smile openly at each other, a recognition spreading itself between them.

"See ya later."

"Bye," Lucía disengages herself in order to get on with her day.

Around noon, a knock on the door disrupts her as she mulls a word in the dictionary. Shit, she mutters and opens it.

"Cave Boy," she says, laughing.

"Are you going to be home tonight?" Jess asks, looking slightly amused and actually tolerant.

"Yup."

"How about if I come by with a pizza?"

"Sure, I'll make a salad."

"See you around six?"

"Sure."

Oh god, here we go again, she says to herself. But her heart is flapping and turning over in a languid manner, and that's always a very good sign. It's spring, it's spring, no wonder I'm so raw, she thinks. I have cells, squirming and stretching, that I forgot I possessed, and she laughs right out loud, surprising the silent air and delighting herself in the process.

When Lucía first left her husband, she felt vacated — not in the hollow, good way of a flute, but vacant, burned up, swallowed up, dispossessed. Must be why my body went and got pregnant. So typically feminine, this body of mine. She will not listen to reason, that's for sure: only feeling. And *she* was feeling like filling up some space and having a baby. Lucía watches her child's awkward attempts to stand. This, she muses, is the orderly miracle of chaos, unbearable passions, the seemingly endless war of women and men. When they lay down their arms, in the secret recesses of the dark cell chamber, and greet each other. Yes, I could've had an abortion, but I'm glad you're here now. She smiles at the child, and he falls on his ass, churning his legs and arms to stand and regain his balance.

I doubt that I'll ever do it again, though, Lucía says directly to her body, her whole-self body. I sure miss my walking-around freedome from time to time.

A little before six Jess knocks a medium knock of happy rhythm: I've got a pizza in my hands, and it's hot and delicious.

"That smells great." Lucía notes he looks flushed and vulnerable.

"I drove about 110 mph getting here. I actually risked my life."

"I love it," Lucía laughs huskily, and again wants to make love to him anywhere handy. This time she accepts this rush all through her body. "Okay, the salad's ready. I must've known this would be life or death. Do you like artichokes? I made some."

Jess nods, and Lucía places everything in a pleasing way on the table. Mayonnaise in a sea shell, a red tablecloth, wine glasses with see-through edges all around holding the late, spring light as easily as the chill, white wine to come.

"Ready," Lucía shouts to Jess in the bathroom. Instantly, he's tearing pizza slices onto plates, biting his before it hits the table.

"What a slob!"

He laughs and growls, and Lucía meows like a cat and scratches the air between them playfully. They exchange a few more growls and cat sounds, laughing like idiots, and then dig into the food.

The wine is glinting and showing off how cold it is, making the glass sweat. The salad is a rainbow of lettuce, tomatoes, carrots, and sliced eggs, slippery with oil. The artichokes are dangerous on the outside and so tender on the inside. Lucía devours two slices of pizza, in a hurry, to Jess's four. Then they slow down for the salad and to strip down the huge, tempting artichokes.

Lucía throws an arthichoke leaf into Jess's wine glass and makes it, perfectly.

"Hey," Jess yells. He throws one back and misses.

Again, she throws and makes it, laughing wide and wicked.

Again, he throws and misses. "Shit! What's your trick?"

"Concentration, my eaglet," she roars.

They begin eating the artichokes quickly, throwing them as soon as they're empty of flesh. Jess's glass is filling, hers is empty. Lucía's laugh is beyond control now.

"Wait a minute," Jess commands and takes out all her leaves. In the lull she catches her breath, and he lands one in her glass.

"You cheated, didn't you?" Lucía shouts. "You reached right over and just plopped it in."

She imitates, exaggeratedly, what he must've looked like, with a hilarious desperation even Jess can't resist. He howls with laughter, and then he puts his whole artichoke into her glass.

"You asshole," she screams. And she puts the whole bowl of salad on his head, the beautiful salad dripping down his neck.

"You're crazy," he runs to the sink, laughing, throwing off the bowl and grabbing a towel. He fills up a glass of water, turns around suddenly and dumps it on her.

She grabs the towel from him and throws it on the floor and begins to wipe up the water, saying, "I just love to dance. I must thank you for this opportunity."

Jess sits and watches her with an intense pleasure that makes her blush.

Lucía changes her clothes and returns to find the table cleared and fresh wine in their glasses.

"Thanks," she says softly.

"My pleasure," he offers. He offers, but won't move forward or touch her.

Is he numb, Lucía wonders? He doesn't know what to do, she answers herself. Well, I refuse to out and out seduce him, her breath rushes out. His, too; the tension in his body is swelling his neck.

"Look, I'm going out for a run. How about if I come back later tonight?"

"Okay," she says, a little on edge.

As Jess leaves she realizes the baby will be up tonight a lot later than usual because of this late nap.

As she clears up she thinks about where she'll go backpacking this summer. She's anxious to see the lakes in these mountains after the especially long winter. I can't wait to sleep outside and watch shooting stars, she affirms.

And then Lucía thinks of her oldest child, her daughter, four years younger than Jess. She thinks of their last get-together, the intensity their reunion always creates. The simple sympathy her daughter's body and presence always provide her, and she provides in return. Their talks long and winding, circular. The memory of her daughter reaching into a lacquered box and taking one of two singular crystal earrings, handing it to her, saying, "Here, take this one, and I'll keep the other."

The love between them, now, spanning great distances, but the single, round crystal earring in one ear (Lucía removes her dangling earrings and locks the crystal into her right ear) never fails to strengthen and comfort her, like the other same-bodied women friends she need only conjure up to freshen her soul at times.

Though there was that year, that one, solitary year, the baby's first year, when the only thing she was able to conjure up was another lost piece of herself. Insanity glared off the walls at times, and she'd tell it, "Fuck you." Putting herself in the deep freeze of the silent, implacable snow, she wrote and fed the baby.

That night a friend calls to come over, but Lucía says she's busy and can't they get together tomorrow? She waits for Jess and he doesn't come at eight or nine or nine-thirty. He finally calls at ten, embarrassed but smooth: "I went out to run, left my keys in my hood. I must've run farther than usual, because by the time I got back it was pitch dark and I couldn't find my keys for shit. So I had to run back home. Anyway, tomorrow I have to go back and find my goddamn keys. Hey, I'm sorry."

"Sounds pretty dramatic and interesting, so it must be okay. Don't worry about it."

"Do you want to go out for dinner tomorrow night?"

"I can't. I'm going over to a friend's."

"How about Friday, then?" Now it's his turn to be suspicious.

"That'd be fine, Jess."

"I'll pick you up at seven?" He relaxes, assured.

"See you then."

"Good night, Lucía." Jess says her name perfectly, to her delight.

"Buenas noches, Jesús."

"What the hell's that?"

"Spanish for Jess. Jesus, like Christ."

"Holy shit. See ya Friday," he says, almost giggling.

"Adiós."

The next night her friend Diane has a gift for her in a pouch—healing herbs, a ring, and a jasper stone. She's an herbalist and a midwife. "Just what I need, believe me," Lucía tells her. Diane is a couple of years older than her daughter, and she knows she still wouldn't be able to be as frank with her own daughter as she is with Diane.

"My god, he's tempting," Lucía mocks herself, holding her heart. "And it's not that I love him, or that I think I will love him; I just want him, pure and simple. I mean, I have feelings for him, but it's not the *big one*. Anyway, it's that clear."

Diane laughs, "Go for it."

"We're a bad influence on each other." They laugh and talk about other things.

The following night, the baby with a friend, Lucía waits for Jess. Dressed up for a change, too, and nervous, she notes. I bet he's nervous as well. I do look a little bit older than him — not much though, she smiles to herself.

Jess drives up in the middle of a purple/peach streaked sunset. Lucía almost forgot he was coming, intent as she was on seeing Venus appear in the darkening sky. The sky is an intense melting of blood colors, and soon Venus will be born, pale and distinct, like magic, she thinks.

"What are you doing?" Jess asks.

"Waiting for Venus to show up," Lucía almost whispers.

Jess sits right across from her on a smaller rock. They sit and wait for Venus to appear in the piercing silence. She can hear Jess breathing and she's glad he's here waiting with her.

"Where do you want to go?" he asks.

"I don't care. How about Mexican food?"

"Good idea," he smiles at her.

"Of course. And you'll love the sangría."

He smiles almost to himself and turns away. "Look. There's your Venus. Pretty bright star."

"It's full moon tonight. When it's a crescent, sometimes Venus gets really close." Lucía pauses and they listen to the silence again. "It's beautiful, isn't it? It's so beautiful."

Jess looks out to the open sky. "You're right," he says. "It sure is."

Lucía gets up and Jess joins her. They walk together to his truck a little awkwardly on the jutting stones that make up her road. He trips and she laughs.

"Be serious, woman."

"Never," Lucía shoots back.

They enter the restaurant and go for the single table with two chairs, with a candle lit and waiting.

"People *are* staring, Jess."

"That's because I'm young and handsome, and you're older and ravishing. Fuck 'em."

"You must be right," Lucía says in a tone of mock sincerity and begins to laugh. In this small town, Lucía knows it's not only that he is younger and she is older, but that she is dark and he is light, and that she looks like she hasn't lost any of her marbles. This thought makes her stop laughing, and instead she proceeds to glow like a light has been turned on.

The waitress comes and they order a whole liter of sangría. It arrives with whole slices of oranges, bananas, and strawberries floating in a cold, red wine.

"How about just having sangreea for dinner?" Jess suggests and means it.

"I'm having a meal. I've been waiting to eat since morning."

"Chicken shit."

"No, I'm not," and she puts a strawberry, whole, into his mouth. He touches her fingers with his wet lips, and they both shiver.

Jess puts a piece of banana into hers, and she licks his fingers quickly. They stare into each other's mouths like famished travellers, knowing the meal will be set before them soon. Lucía catches the eye of an older woman, and she gives Lucía a knowing wink.

On the way home they're silent. They ate everything on their plates and had another half-liter of sangría. As they park, Lucía asks, "Do you want to go for a walk?"

They walk toward the creek, the moon as bright as false noon. They reach the creek and watch the night lights on the water. Then they head back, but Lucía can't bear to leave the sound of the creek yet, so she sits on a log. Jess sits opposite her on another one for a while, then joins her.

"Look, that's Mars. The red planet," Jess points toward it.

"The planet of war and conflict," Lucía murmurs, and she gives it a dead-on stare, then looks away.

"I want to travel," Jess says. "I want to get the hell out of here."

"I do too. I always will. More of Mexico. I want to see Peru, Bali, Africa."

"You're lucky you're an artist. You don't seem so restless."

"Fooled you, didn't I?"

They walk back to the house, arm in arm, a little awkwardly, like they don't quite fit. They hold hands and it feels better.

Inside, Lucía begins to build a fire, but Jess asks her to sit next to him instead. She does. "Closer," he says. She does, and he puts his arm around her and she lays her head on his shoulder. It's late, and she looks up at him, face to face. He looks right back and lets out an involuntary "shit." Jess puts his arms all around her back, pulls her firmly toward him, and kisses her, his lips parted like a rose.

The heat is there immediately, and he's saying inarticulate things, and she's stroking his neck and face. They pause in the warmth between them, cradling one another.

"How about if I take a shower? I didn't take one today after work." He separates himself slightly, grazes her lips with his tongue.

"You smell good to me," Lucía laughs very softly, "but go ahead. First let me get in and brush my teeth." She kisses his eyelids, one by one.

She lays in bed for a minute feeling her body hum. Then Jess starts the shower. She sits up in bed, facing the window and the full moon.

Jess walks into her bedroom and stops at the doorway. "The moonlight is so beautiful in your room," he says with admiration, as though she'd created it.

Silently, Lucía gets up and walks toward Jess and embraces him, his whole body. He's so solid without clothes, she realizes. She takes him by the hand and leads him to her bed. She lets go at the edge and he follows her. As they come together she smells roses. He used the pink rose soap instead of the brown sandlewood, and this moves her over the brink of reason. Their kissing becomes like their laughter, out of control. His lips move down to her nipples, her belly. She tries to pull him back up, into her, briefly, but he continues to move his mouth down into her sex. Moonlight floods the room and their bodies, and his tongue is so soft and persistent. She feels, clearly, he wants this too, he wants this too.

At the point where she reaches the top of the wave, the very top of the wave, before the deep sea dive into her depths, she thinks suddenly, like lightning, "You could be my son." And she dives so deeply she brings up a jewel, her very own treasure.

Lucía pulls him up to her, and Jess laughs, "A little rain, I'm afraid." Slightly embarrassed and apologetic, he adds, "I just couldn't wait."

"Never mind." She feels his semen slide between them, and the sea mixes with the scent of roses. They kiss fully, body to body, and she tells him, "Thank you, Jess. I've never come with a man the first time."

"Thank yourself, lady. You're an intense lady." He looks directly at her, "You really are." He comes near her face, kissing her temples, the edges of her eyes. "I love your hair, your hair . . ."

Jess strokes her back from the nape of her neck to the top of her legs. Lucía does the same to him, and they fall asleep this way as the moon continues its patient journey, as the Earth slightly tilts toward the sun.

The next morning Lucía wakes first with the baby and takes him out into the kitchen. She prepares food for the baby and coffee. She is distracted by light and smell and touch. Everything she touches spreads out from her clitoris, womb, and nipples. The coffee enters her through her cells, it seems. She is hungry for Jess, and she is hungry for food.

Lucía begins to prepare omelettes, her favorite sensual food: golden softness filled with things. Onions, cheese, garlic, jalapeño. Chilled wine would be marvellous, she thinks. Champagne even better. Better? What could be better than the heat between bodies? Silence and light, she answers herself and laughs. One extreme to the other (but not really, she adds).

She's interrupted with: "Look, I'm going down to the job. I'll get some coffee there." Jess isn't looking at her, he's speaking to a stool or the floor, but definitely not her.

"I was just about to make some outrageous omelettes, and the coffee's done, Jess."

"Nah, I'm not hungry."

Lucía walks up to Jess and places her hands on his shoulders, trying to look into his face. "What is it?"

He glares at her. He's closed up and cold. "Hey, I'm really not hungry. Look, I'll see ya later."

"When?"

"Tonight."

"When?"

"About eight," and slams the door against her.

He's embarrassed because he came to soon. He's embarrassed because he's young. He's embarrassed because I know, she thinks. It helps a little, but not much, because she feels disappointed, abruptly hurt, and angry.

Lucía wrestles with this all day, through the baby, her work, the mundane cleanup, the shifting of light and wind and silence. She decides to be patient. She imagines him drinking the instant coffee with relief, driving the nails in too hard, laughing harshly with his friends, and ridding himself of her. Afraid. She also remembers the gentleness of the night and decides to be understanding. Now she's afraid.

Jess doesn't come at eight but at ten, with a friend. It's raining pretty hard, and she's fallen asleep by the fire. She's showered and washed her hair and feels very good in her body. The knock pulls her out of sleep. She feels dreamy and the sight of him angers her. She sees his friend standing in the rain and asks him in.

"Rather late, aren't you, Jess?"

"Hey, we're all going to Tahoe. Get ready. We're taking off right now."

"I can't go, Jess, and you know it," Lucía stares at him, slowly, with an obviously controlled anger.

"That's a bummer having to take care of a kid every day." He looks at her with satisfaction.

"Someone took care of you. Someone took the damn time to take care of you every damn day. It's part of the human experience," and she almost says it, Cave Boy.

"Hey, I'll catch ya later," ashamed now by the presence of a witness.

"Don't count on it. Good night, Dave," she says to his friend, and slams the door shut.

After that, they passed each other in their cars a few times and he'd smile like a fool and wave at her. She was torn between waving at the boyish greeting and flipping him off. She just passed by, keeping her eyes straight ahead. He never had the courage to call or stop by. Then she never saw him again.

After that, she dreamt his pick-up truck was parked by an immense cave, and, in the dream, she wondered where he was. And then she knew he had entered the cave, that mother, though he had not entered her. And she knew this was her gift to him.

Lucía's husband had given her the mastery of the masculine. And Jess, Jess gave her the freedom. The gift of the son.

The Authors

The Authors

MARJORIE AGOSIN, born in 1955, is a Chilean poet who has been living in the United States since 1970. She is presently an assistant professor of Latin American literature at Wellesley College. She has published essays dealing with Hispanic women writers and three books of poetry: *Chile: Gemidos y cantares* (1977), *Conchalí* (1980), and *Silencio que se deja oír* (1982).

GLORIA ANZALDUA, a Tejana Chicana poet, is co-editor of *This Bridge Called My Back: Writings By Radical Women of Color* (Kitchen Table Women of Color Press, 1983). Her work has appeared in *Cuentos: Stories by Latinas, Conditions,* and *Sinister Wisdom.* She is currently working on a book of short stories, *El Mundo Zurdo and Other Stories.*

ANDREA-TERESA ARENAS is a Chicana writer currently living in Milwaukee where she is an administrator at Alverno College and where she hosts a PBS monthly television series, "Nuestro Milwaukee." She has had creative literature published or accepted in *Revista Chicano-Riqueña, Third Woman,* and *Women of Color News.*

ROSA MARIA ARENAS is the author of a chapbook of poems entitled *She Said Yes* (Fallen Angel Press, 1981). Her poems have appeared in *Passages North, The Red Cedar Review, 13th Moon, Skywriting,* and *Ikon,* among others. She was a featured poet at the 1980 Michigan Poetry Festival and is currently Managing Editor of *Labyris,* a woman's literary arts journal at Michigan State University.

MIRIAM BORNSTEIN does not consider herself a poet; rather, she sees herself as a cultural worker dedicated to teaching and writing poetry and critical studies on Chicano and Latin American literature. She received her Ph.D. in Spanish from the University of Arizona in 1982 and has published her poetry in book form (*Bajo cubierta*, 1976), in anthologies, and in literary magazines.

ANA CASTILLO has published three chapbooks of poetry: *Otro canto* (1977), *The Invitation* (1979), and *Women Are Not Roses* (1985). In 1982 her musical adaptation of *The Invitation* premiered as part of the First Soho Art Festival in New York City. Her novel *The Mixquiahuala Letters* is forthcoming (spring 1986) from Bilingual Review/Press.

INA CUMPIANO is a Puerto Rican poet and translator currently at the University of Iowa. She has advanced degrees from the University of Northern Colorado and from Johns Hopkins University. She has translated Leopoldo Marechal's *Días como flechas* and Alberti's *Poemas de Punta del Este.* Her own work has appeared in *Antioch Review* and *The Bilingual Review/La Revista Bilingüe.*

MARIA HERRERA-SOBEK is presently Associate Professor in the Department of Spanish and Portuguese at the University of California, Irvine. Recent publications include: *The Bracero Experience: Elitelore Versus Folklore* (1979), *Beyond Stereotypes: The Critical Analysis of Chicana Literature* (1985), and articles on Chicano folklore and literature. Her poetry has appeared in *Chasqui, Revista Chicano-Riqueña,* and various literary anthologies.

CAROLINA MATA DE WOODRUFF is one of fourteen children born to migrant farmworkers from Crystal City, Texas. Carolina has migrated with her family to work in the fields all her life. Traveling great distances for the "opportunity" to earn sub-minimum wages, the Mata family has worked up and down the West Coast stream and the Great Plains and Midwest stream. By means of Federal Department of Labor, Office of Education Migrant Programs and a determination to make a better life for herself and her family, Carolina graduated from high school, attended the CAMP program at St. Edwards University, and completed a B.A. in Accounting and Business Administration at Antioch University-West in Los Angeles, California. This is her first publication.

PAT MORA is the author of the poetry collection *Chants* (Arte Público Press, 1983). In 1983 she received a creative writing award from the National Association for Chicano Studies. She is Assistant to the Vice President for Academic Affairs at the University of Texas at El Paso.

BARBARA MUJICA is a professor of Spanish at Georgetown University. Her fiction has appeared in numerous publications, including *Women: A Journal of Liberation, Letras femeninas, The Antietam Review, Término, Crop Dust, Corridors Literary Magazine,* and *Verbena: Bilingual Review of the Arts,* of which she is the editor. She also has numerous scholarly publications.

ACHY OBEJAS is a young Cuban poet and writer currently writing for a variety of publications, including *The Chicago Reporter, The Chicago Reader,* and *The Logan Square Free Press.* Her work has appeared in *The Beloit Poetry Journal, Antigonish Review, Sinister Wisdom, Third Woman, Ecos, Revista Chicano-Riqueña,* and many others. A play she co-wrote, "Carnicería," ran from February to August 1983 to critical praise and is considered the most successful play in the history of Spanish-language theatre in Chicago.

JUDITH ORTIZ COFER has published poetry in numerous journals and is the author of three chapbooks of poetry: *Latin Women Pray* (Florida Arts Gazette Press, 1980), *The Native Dancer* (Pteranodon Press, 1981), and *Among the Ancestors* (Louisville News Press, 1981). In 1981 she was awarded a Fellowship in Literature by The Fine Arts Council of Florida. She currently teaches at the University of Georgia, and her collection of poems *Reaching for the Mainland* will be published in 1986 by Bilingual Review/Press.

RAQUEL PUIG ZALDIVAR, a Cuban-American writer residing in Florida, has had her work published in *Caritas, The Bilingual Review/La Revista Bilingüe, El Miami Herald, Nuestro, Diario Las Américas, Revista Iberoamericana,* and many other outlets. She teaches at Miami Dade Community College.

MAGALY QUIÑONES, born in Ponce, Puerto Rico, is the author of *Entre mi voz y el tiempo* (poems, 1969), *Era que el mundo era* (poems, 1974), *Zumbayllu* (poems, 1976), *Cosas de poetas, cosas nuestras* (letters, 1977), *Cantándole a la noche misma* (poems, 1978), and *En la pequeña Antilla* (poems, 1982). Her collection "Nombrar" won second prize in the poetry competition sponsored by the magazine *Mairena* in 1982.

DIANA RIVERA writes poetry and short stories and has exhibited her paintings throughout New York and in Puerto Rico. Her poems have appeared in *Chelsea, Central Park,* the *John O'Hara Journal,* and the *Princeton Spectrum,* among others. Her short fiction has appeared in *Hispanics in the United States: An Anthology of Creative Literature*. She lives with her husband on a farm in northeastern Pennsylvania.

SONIA RIVERA-VALDES, born in Güines, Cuba, currently lives in New York, where she teaches and is writing her doctoral dissertation on Puerto Rican literature. She has previously published in *Punto de Vista* and *Areito*.

ELIANA RIVERO was born in Artemisa, Cuba, and has lived in the United States since 1961. She began writing poetry in 1968 and has had two volumes of her work appear: *De cal y arena* (1975) and *Cuerpos breves* (1976). She also coedited the anthology *Siete poetas* (1978) with the Chicana poet and critic Margarita Cota Cárdenas. Rivero's poems have been published in such anthologies and journals as *Antología poética hispanoamericana*, *Canto al pueblo*, *Mester*, *Chasqui*, *The Denver Quarterly*, *International Poetry Review*, *Revista Chicano-Riqueña*, and many others.

MARTA SALINAS, born in Coalinga, California, in 1949, has a M.F.A. in Creative Writing from the University of California, Irvine. Two of her stories, "When the Alphabet Spoke" and "Rounds," appeared in the *Los Angeles Herald Examiner* in May and June of 1983, and a third, "Kisses are Dangerous," was published in the weekly *California Living* in February 1984. She is working on her first novel, *Yolanda*.

MIRIAM DE URIARTE's work has been published in *The Southern Poetry Review*, *Transfer Magazine*, *Hispanics in the United States: An Anthology of Creative Literature*, *The Berkeley Monthly*, and a number of local magazines. She holds an M.A. degree in creative writing from San Francisco State University. She directs a children's art school, The Berkeley Child Art Studio, which she founded in 1970, and lectures widely on Mexican culture and art.

ALMA VILLANUEVA is the author of *Bloodroot* (1977), *Mother, May I?* (1978), *Life Span* (1984), and *La Chingada* (in *Five Poets of Aztlán*, 1985). She was the first place winner of the Third Chicano Literary Prize (1977) at the University of California, Irvine. She has been anthologized in *The Next World, Contemporary Women Poets, I Sing a Song to Myself, Beyond Rice*, both volumes of *Hispanics in the United States: An Anthology of Creative Literature*, and *Women Writing Poetry in America*.

HELENA MARIA VIRAMONTES was born and raised in East Los Angeles into a family of nine brothers and sisters. She has published in *Statement Magazine, Maize, Xhisme-Arte*, and the anthology *Cuentos: Stories by Latinas*. Her collection *The Moths and Other Stories* appeared in 1985.